The Bathroom Trivia ALMANAC

CONTRIBUTORS

Compiled by: Russ "The Flush" Edwards

"Head" Editor: Ellen Fischbein

Significant Others:
Angela Demers
Jack Kreismer
Geoff Scowcroft

Cover and Page Design
s.w.artz, inc.

RED-LETTER PRESS, INC.
Saddle River, New Jersey

INTRODUCTION

In these tumultuous times, the bathroom has become a safe haven for peace – one good reason why restroom reading is on a roll.

Proof of this privial pursuit comes from the findings of "The Toilet Paper Report"* (subtitled "What's Happening in Today's Bathroom") which reveals that reading is the third most time-consuming activity behind that closed door, trailing only bathing and showering.

Further, the Scott Paper Company, makers of the toilet tissue, reports that bathroom reading is linked with higher seats of learning. They conducted a recent survey which concluded that more than two-thirds of people holding master's degrees and doctorates read in the bathroom.

And so it is that we at Red-Letter Press continue to add to the loo's literary cause with our latest "Bathroom Library" book, "The Bathroom Trivia Almanac". The 365 day format makes it ideal for the regular reader—the quintessential almanac for the Quincy!**

Yours flushingly,

Jack Kreismer
Publisher

*Yes, there really is such a document. It's published by the manufacturers of Quilted Northern toilet tissue.

**For those not privy to the term, the bathroom became known as the Quincy back in the days when President John Quincy Adams had a bathroom installed in the White House.

JANUARY 1st

TODAY'S THOUGHT: "This is the year you expected so much from last year." —*Ed Howe*

HISTORY: On this date in 1863 President Lincoln issued the Emancipation Proclamation, a document freeing all slaves in areas still in rebellion.

QUIZ: What day preceded January 1st as New Year's Day in English speaking countries?

Trivia

All race horses celebrate their birthdays on New Year's Day, no matter when they were born.

QUIZ ANSWER: January 1st has kicked off the New Year in English speaking countries since the adoption of the British Calendar Act of 1751. Prior to that, the New Year began on March 25th.

JANUARY 2nd

TODAY'S THOUGHT: "Never raise your hand to your children — it leaves your midsection unprotected." —*Fred Allen*

HISTORY: On this date in 1959 Soviet space probe Luna I missed the moon and went into orbit around the sun. All those years we sweated their missiles and these guys missed the MOON!!

QUIZ: A certain southpaw pitcher was given a tryout by the Washington Senators in the 1950's. He didn't make the team and he's been having nothing but trouble with Washington ever since. Who is he?

Trivia

If you like to engage in many sesquipedalianisms, you like to use big words.

QUIZ ANSWER: Fidel Castro

JANUARY 3rd

TODAY'S THOUGHT: "Laughter is the shortest distance between two people." —*Victor Borge*

HISTORY: On this date in 1888 the U.S. Patent Office issued a patent for artificial drinking straws.

QUIZ: What long running game show was pivotal in Mel Gibson's life?

Trivia
The eyes of some birds weigh more than their brains.

QUIZ ANSWER: "Jeopardy!" — Mel was born in the States, but when the turbulent sixties came around, his dad wanted to give things a try "Down Under". He went on "Jeopardy!" to win enough money to move the family to Australia.

JANUARY 4th

TODAY'S THOUGHT: "Hospitals are weird. They put you in a private room and then give you a public gown."
—*Milton Berle*

HISTORY: On this date in 1493 Columbus began his journey back to Spain to report his discovery.

QUIZ: Bathroom Brain Teaser: Which can see better in total darkness — an owl, a raccoon or a skunk?

Trivia
During her lifetime only seven of Emily Dickinson's poems were published. Approximately 1,770 completed and fragmented poems were found after her death in 1886.

QUIZ ANSWER: None of them can see in total darkness.

JANUARY 5th

TODAY'S THOUGHT: "If you want to talk to somebody who's not busy, call the Vice President. I get plenty of time to talk to anybody about anything." —*Walter Mondale*

HISTORY: On this date in 1893 an Austrian newspaper reported the enormous potential of X-rays.

QUIZ: Who is the last president that didn't attend college?

Trivia
Mozart wrote the nursery rhyme tune "Twinkle, Twinkle, Little Star" at the age of five.

QUIZ ANSWER: Harry S. Truman

JANUARY 6th

TODAY'S THOUGHT: "Slang is a language that rolls up its sleeves, spits on his hands, and goes back to work." —*Carl Sandburg*

HISTORY: On this date in 1942 the first around-the-world trip by a commercial airliner was completed... but the luggage was never found.

QUIZ: What long running classic sitcom got its start on the Danny Thomas show, "Make Room For Daddy"?

Trivia
Saudi Arabia refused to carry the "Muppet Show" on television because one of the stars was a pig.

QUIZ ANSWER: The "Andy Griffith Show" — The sheriff of Mayberry was first seen on an episode of "Make Room For Daddy".

JANUARY 7th

TODAY'S THOUGHT: "An honorable defeat is better than a dishonorable victory." —*Millard Fillmore*

HISTORY: On this date in 1610 Galileo discovered the four largest moons of Jupiter.

QUIZ: American soldiers have often been referred to as "G.I.'s". What does G.I. stand for?

Trivia

President James Garfield was ambidextrous and could write with both hands simultaneously.

QUIZ ANSWER: "General Issue", the term stamped on their clothing, equipment and supplies (In some quarters it is referred to as "Government Issue".)

JANUARY 8th

TODAY'S THOUGHT: "Be true to your teeth and they won't be false to you." —*Soupy Sales*

HISTORY: On this date in 1935 Elvis Presley was born.

QUIZ: What do Clint Reno, Tulsa McCauley, Glenn Tyler, Josh Morgan, Vince Everett, Joe Lightcloud and Jesse Wade have in common?

Trivia

Elvis was once appointed Special Agent of the Bureau of Narcotics and Dangerous Drugs.

QUIZ ANSWER: They were all characters that Elvis played in his movies. By the way, the name on Elvis' birth certificate reads "Elvis Aron Presley", a misspelling that was later corrected.

JANUARY 9th

TODAY'S THOUGHT: "I have often thought that if there had been a good rap group around in those days, I might have chosen a career in music instead of politics."
—*Richard M. Nixon*

HISTORY: On this date in 1793 the first successful American balloon flight was made from Philadelphia to New Jersey, piloted by Jean Pierre Blanchard.

QUIZ: How many sides are there on a dodecagon?

Trivia
"1812 Overture" composer Tchaikovsky suffered from nervous disorders and hallucinations and had a morbid fear that his head would roll off his shoulders while conducting the orchestra.

QUIZ ANSWER: Twelve

JANUARY 10th

TODAY'S THOUGHT: "Boxing is sort of like jazz. The better it is, the less amount of people can appreciate it."
—*George Foreman*

HISTORY: On this date in 1776 Thomas Paine published "Common Sense".

QUIZ: When is a band-aid a band-aid?

Trivia
It wasn't until the Civil War that specific left and right shoes were made.

QUIZ ANSWER: Only when it is made by Johnson and Johnson — Though we commonly refer to an adhesive bandage by the name, J & J holds the trademark on it.

JANUARY 11th

TODAY'S THOUGHT: "A national debt, if it's not excessive, will be to us a national blessing."
—*Alexander Hamilton*

HISTORY: On this date in 1973 the American League voted to adopt the "designated hitter" rule.

QUIZ: Who was Major League baseball's first designated hitter?

Trivia

It is 127 feet, 3-3/8 inches from home plate to second base on a big league diamond.

QUIZ ANSWER: New York Yankee Ron Blomberg, who was walked by Red Sox pitcher, Luis Tiant, on April 6, 1973

JANUARY 12th

TODAY'S THOUGHT: "You're only young once but you can be immature forever." —*Anonymous*

HISTORY: On this date in 1922 Hattie Caraway became the first female U.S. Senator.

QUIZ: What does "Mardi Gras" mean?

Trivia

The Indian on the Indian head penny was not an Indian at all. The model was Sarah Longacre, a relative of one of the mint's officials.

QUIZ ANSWER: Literally translated, it means "Fat Tuesday".

JANUARY 13th

TODAY'S THOUGHT: "A hospital bed is a parked taxi with the meter running." —*Groucho Marx*

HISTORY: On this date in 1920 a "New York Times" editorial opined that rockets would never fly.

QUIZ: During the course of a lifetime, the average American...

A: eats 269 gallons of ice cream

B: makes nearly 200,000 phone calls

C: sleeps about 23 years

D: all of the above

E: none of the above

Trivia
Americans eat about 12 billion bananas each year.

QUIZ ANSWER: D — And they take about 10,000 stupid multiple choice tests!!

JANUARY 14th

TODAY'S THOUGHT: "Go to bed. What you're staying up for isn't worth it." —*Andy Rooney*

HISTORY: On this date in 1952 the "Today" show premiered on NBC.

QUIZ: EWR, LAX, DFW and ORD are flighty abbreviations for what?

Trivia
Robert Todd Lincoln was present at three presidential assassinations — his father's, President Garfield's and President McKinley's.

QUIZ ANSWER: Airports — EWR is Newark Airport; LAX is Los Angeles; DFW is Dallas-Fort Worth; and ORD is for O'Hare in Chicago (from the old Orchard Field).

JANUARY 15th

TODAY'S THOUGHT: "One thing about baldness—it's neat." —*Don Herold*

HISTORY: On this date in 1870 "Harper's Weekly" introduced the donkey as the symbol of the Democratic Party.

QUIZ: One-day-wonder George Willig climbed the 110 story south tower of the World Trade Center in New York in 1977. Then Mayor Abraham Beame fined him for his misconduct. How much was he fined?

A: $110,000   B: $11,000   C: $1,100   D: $1.10

Trivia

If you want to go from the ground floor to the top of the Empire State Building on foot, get ready for 1,575 steps.

QUIZ ANSWER: D — A penny for every floor

JANUARY 16th

TODAY'S THOUGHT: "My father told me all about the birds and the bees. The liar — I went steady with a woodpecker till I was twenty-one." —*Bob Hope*

HISTORY: On this date in 1920 prohibition became the law of the land and America went dry.

QUIZ: What is the plural of praying mantis?

Trivia

At the outbreak of WWI, the American Air Force consisted of only 50 men. Of course that wasn't so bad considering they only had one plane!

QUIZ ANSWER: Praying mantid

JANUARY 17th

TODAY'S THOUGHT: "Anger is never without a Reason, seldom with a good One." —*Benjamin Franklin*

HISTORY: On this date in 1871 Andrew Hallidie was issued a patent for the first cable car.

QUIZ: What popular beverage was introduced in 1929 as Bib-Label Lithiated Lemon-Lime soda?

Trivia

The world's record for keeping a Lifesaver in the mouth with the hole intact is 7 hours and 10 minutes.

QUIZ ANSWER: Imagine having to write a jingle for that name! Fortunately the bottlers wised up and rechristened the drink 7-Up.

JANUARY 18th

TODAY'S THOUGHT: "It's no longer a question of staying healthy. It's a question of finding a sickness you like." —*Jackie Mason*

HISTORY: On this date in 1986 it was the first observance of Martin Luther King Jr.'s birth as a legal public holiday.

QUIZ: Does a zebra have white or black stripes?

Trivia

If all the ice in Antarctica melted it would raise the water level of the world's oceans over two hundred feet.

QUIZ ANSWER: It has black stripes on a white or gtawny body.

JANUARY 19th

TODAY'S THOUGHT: "The way I see it, if you want the rainbow, you gotta put up with the rain." —*Dolly Parton*

HISTORY: On this date in 1977 President Ford pardoned Tokyo Rose. She had been convicted of treason for her broadcasts during World War II.

QUIZ: What job did Robert E. Lee turn down to accept command of the Confederate forces?

Trivia

Edgar Allen Poe was expelled from West Point in 1831 when he appeared at a parade in his birthday suit.

QUIZ ANSWER: Lee declined command of the Union forces. He apparently felt his loyalty was to his home state of Virginia.

JANUARY 20th

TODAY'S THOUGHT: "By the time you're eighty years old, you've learned everything. You only have to remember it." —*George Burns*

HISTORY: On this date in 1981 Ronald Reagan became president on the same day the Iranian crisis ended with the release of 52 American hostages.

QUIZ: Don't get a headache over it, but can you figure out the common name for $C_9H_8O_4$?

Trivia

In 1952 Queen Elizabeth was named "Time" magazine's "Man of the Year".

QUIZ ANSWER: Aspirin (acetylsalicylic acid)

JANUARY 21st

TODAY'S THOUGHT: "It's hard not to play golf that's up to Jack Nicklaus standards when you are Jack Nicklaus." —*Jack Nicklaus*

HISTORY: On this date in 1908 New York City passed a regulation making it illegal for women to smoke in public.

QUIZ: Bathroom Brain Teaser: A female dog had three puppies. Two of them were named Moe and Larry. What was the third puppy's name.

Trivia
Miniature golf was originally called "Tom Thumb Golf".

QUIZ ANSWER: What (Feel like a Stooge?)

JANUARY 22nd

TODAY'S THOUGHT: "The cat could very well be man's best friend but would never stoop to admitting it." —*Doug Larson*

HISTORY: On this date in 1901 the Victorian era ended when the Queen died at age 82.

QUIZ: Bathroom Brain Teaser: A man rode a horse from New York to Los Angeles. He left on Wednesday and arrived on the very same Wednesday. How is that?

Trivia
The ten most popular cat names, in order, are: Kitty, Smokey, Shadow, Tiger, Boo, Boots, Molly, Tigger, Spike and Princess.

QUIZ ANSWER: The horse's name was Wednesday.

JANUARY 23rd

TODAY'S THOUGHT: "A medium, so called because it is neither rare nor well done."
—*Ernie Kovacs, on television*

HISTORY: On this date in 1849 Elizabeth Blackwell became the first female medical doctor.

QUIZ: Everybody knows that Humphrey Bogart's character in "Casablanca" was named Rick, but what was his last name?

Trivia

There are no armed forces in the nations of Iceland, Costa Rica or Lichtenstein.

QUIZ ANSWER: You must remember this...the name was Blaine.

JANUARY 24th

TODAY'S THOUGHT: "Start every day with a smile and get it over with." —*W.C. Fields*

HISTORY: On this date in 1848 the California gold rush began when nuggets were discovered at Sutter's Mill.

QUIZ: Who was the first woman to appear on the cover of a Wheaties box?

Trivia

Some species of bamboo can grow up to three feet in a single day.

QUIZ ANSWER: Mary Lou Retton, the Olympic gold medal gymnast, made her "Breakfast of Champions" appearance in 1984.

JANUARY 25th

TODAY'S THOUGHT: "They should put expiration dates on clothes so we would know when they go out of style."
—*Gary Shandling*

HISTORY: On this date in 1940 the first Social Security checks went out in the mail. Most of them have probably been delivered by now.

QUIZ: If you were heading south from Detroit, what is the first foreign country you would arrive in?

Trivia

The very first group to appear on Dick Clark's "American Bandstand" was the Chordettes.

QUIZ ANSWER: Canada

JANUARY 26th

TODAY'S THOUGHT: "My wife's final decision seldom tallies with the one immediately following it."
—*Paul Newman*

HISTORY: On this date in 1784 Benjamin Franklin declared that he wanted the turkey, rather than the eagle, as the U.S. symbol.

QUIZ: Can you identify the foreign capital named after the fifth U.S. president and the country where it's located?

Trivia

A law which was (and may still be!) on the books — You're not allowed to remove your shoes if your feet smell while you're in the theater in Winnetlea, Illinois.

QUIZ ANSWER: Monrovia, Liberia

JANUARY 27th

TODAY'S THOUGHT: "Early to rise and early to bed, makes a man healthy, wealthy and dead."
—James Thurber

HISTORY: On this date in 1880 Thomas Edison got his patent for one of his brightest ideas — the electric light bulb!

QUIZ: Can you name the only airline with a name composed of three consecutive letters?

Trivia

Grover Cleveland had an artificial jaw made out of rubber. All politicians have been known to stretch a point, but this was ridiculous!

QUIZ ANSWER: KLM

JANUARY 28th

TODAY'S THOUGHT: "There are only three basic jokes, but since the mother-in-law is not a joke but a very serious question, there are only two." *—George Ade*

HISTORY: On this date in 1986 the space shuttle *Challenger* exploded, 74 seconds into flight, killing the seven crew members.

QUIZ: Knowing that the Addams family is a little weird, what do you think little Wednesday's middle name is?

Trivia

Most of the germs that get into your body enter through your mouth.

QUIZ ANSWER: Thursday — Just think, if she married Joe Friday, she'd be....

JANUARY 29th

TODAY'S THOUGHT: "I was born into it and there was nothing I could do about it. It was there, like air or food, or any other element. The only question with wealth is what you do with it." —*John D. Rockefeller, Jr.*

HISTORY: On this date in 1900 baseball's American League got its start.

QUIZ: Within a hundred pounds or so, if you wanted to steal a billion dollars in $100 bills, how much weight would you have to be prepared to carry?

Trivia
There are 293 ways to make change for a dollar.

QUIZ ANSWER: A billion bucks in C-notes would be some seriously heavy bread. In fact, it would weigh about 10 tons!

JANUARY 30th

TODAY'S THOUGHT: "I belong to Bridegrooms Anonymous. Whenever I feel like getting married, they send over a lady in a housecoat and hair curlers to burn my toast for me." —*Dick Martin*

HISTORY: On this date in 1969 the Beatles played together publicly for the final time on the roof of their Apple Studios.

QUIZ: What was the first U.S. network show to introduce the Beatles to America?

Trivia
A Matisse, "Le Bateau", was hung upside down for a month and a half in the Museum of Modern Art in New York before anyone noticed.

QUIZ ANSWER: The Fab Four were actually featured on tape in January, 1964 on "The Jack Paar Show".

JANUARY 31st

TODAY'S THOUGHT: "There are two great rules of life: never tell everything at once." —*Ken Venturi*

HISTORY: On this date in 1958 the U.S. launched its first satellite, Explorer I, an event that lead directly to our modern world of defense, weather and communications satellites.

QUIZ: They are manufactured in Topeka, Kansas. They measure eleven and one half feet across, weigh 12,500 pounds and cost over $50,000. What are they?

Trivia

Alaska was bought from Russia for about two cents an acre.

QUIZ ANSWER: The largest tires that Goodyear makes, they fit on giant dump trucks.

FEBRUARY 1st

TODAY'S THOUGHT: "Remember, a closed mouth gathers no foot." —*Steve Frost*

HISTORY: On this date in 1892 the term "400" first came into use in snobbery circles when the queen of New York's social scene, Mrs. William Astor, held a ball at her mansion. Four hundred was the maximum number that her ballroom could accommodate.

QUIZ: Admiral Byrd took along a refrigerator on his expedition to the Antarctic. Why?

Trivia

Julius Caesar's autograph is worth $2 million.

QUIZ ANSWER: To keep the crew's food from freezing since the refrigerator was warmer than the outside temperature

FEBRUARY 2nd

TODAY'S THOUGHT: "I'm no different from anybody else with two arms, two legs and forty-two hundred hits." —*Pete Rose*

HISTORY: On this date in 1876 eight teams joined together to form baseball's National League.

QUIZ: February is National Weddings Month. Can you say "I do" to the following question? Do you know what the bride walks down in church during the wedding ceremony?

Trivia

Less than half of the single men in the U.S. who've reached the age of 35 ever get married.

QUIZ ANSWER: Aisle? No, not quite. The aisles of a church are on the sides. The center path through the pews is called the nave.

FEBRUARY 3rd

TODAY'S THOUGHT: "If you are ever in doubt as to whether you should kiss a pretty girl, always give her the benefit of the doubt." —*Thomas Carlyle*

HISTORY: On this date in 1913 the Sixteenth Amendment was ratified. That's what gave Congress the power to levy income taxes. Planning any celebration?

QUIZ: Norman Rockwell illustrated 317 covers over a 47 year period for what magazine?

Trivia

George Washington earned $25,000 a year as president of the U.S.

QUIZ ANSWER: "The Saturday Evening Post"

FEBRUARY 4th

TODAY'S THOUGHT: "If your parents didn't have any children, there's a good chance that you won't have any." —*Clarence Day*

HISTORY: On this date in 1941 the USO was founded.

QUIZ: Buffalo Bill Cody gave what sharpshooter the nickname "Little Sure Shot"?

Trivia

Charles Lindbergh was not the first person to cross the Atlantic in an airplane. Sixty-six people made the trip before he did. He was the first to fly alone.

QUIZ ANSWER: Annie Oakley

FEBRUARY 5th

TODAY'S THOUGHT: "Flattery is alright, if you don't inhale." —*Adlai Stevenson*

HISTORY: On this date in 1985 the longest war in history ended. The Third Punic War, between Rome and Carthage, was officially settled with a treaty — 2,131 years after it began.

QUIZ: Who walks faster, a man or a woman?

Trivia
Clark Gable's U.S. military discharge papers were signed by Major Ronald Reagan.

QUIZ ANSWER: According to a University of Minnesota, Duluth study, a woman does. The average woman walks 256 feet per minute while a man walks about 245.

FEBRUARY 6th

TODAY'S THOUGHT: "I have never hated a man enough to give his diamonds back." —*Zsa Zsa Gabor*

HISTORY: On this date in 1971 Alan Shepard played golf on the moon.

QUIZ: What do James I of Scotland, Henry III of France, King Edward Ironsides of England and Catherine the Great of Russia have in common?

Trivia
As many as 100 pearls have been found in a single oyster.

QUIZ ANSWER: The last throne they ever sat upon was in a bathroom. By the way, Charles I of Spain was the only king ever born in a bathroom.

FEBRUARY 7th

TODAY'S THOUGHT: "Somebody said to me, 'But the Beatles were antimaterialistic.' That is a huge myth. John and I literally used to sit down and say, 'Now, let's write a swimming pool.'" —*Paul McCartney*

HISTORY: On this date in 1964 the British invasion began as those lovable moptops from Liverpool, the Beatles, landed on U.S. shores.

QUIZ: What two movies have won the most Oscars?

Trivia
Shirley Temple had exactly 56 curls in her hair.

QUIZ ANSWER: "Ben Hur" and "Titanic", 11

FEBRUARY 8th

TODAY'S THOUGHT: "Either this man is dead or my watch has stopped." —*Groucho Marx*

HISTORY: On this date in 1910 the Boy Scouts of America did their first good deed as they were founded.

QUIZ: Which of the following prominent Americans, all born on February 8, was actually born in Lancashire, England?

Jules Verne, Jack Lemmon, James Dean,
Ted Koppel, Robert Klein, Nick Nolte

Trivia
Erma Bombeck began her career as an obituary writer for Ohio's "Dayton Journal-Herald".

QUIZ ANSWER: Born "across the pond" in jolly Olde England was none other than "Nightline" anchorman, Ted Koppel.

FEBRUARY 9th

TODAY'S THOUGHT: "I have everything now I had twenty years ago — except now it's all lower."
—*Gypsy Rose Lee*

HISTORY: On this date in 1895 volleyball was invented by W.G. Morgan of Holyoke, Massachusetts.

QUIZ: What is William Henry Harrison's chief distinction as Chief Executive?

Trivia

A chow is the only dog without a pink tongue; it is black.

QUIZ ANSWER: Harrison served the shortest time of any elected president — 32 days. He died of pneumonia contracted during his dank and cold inauguration.

FEBRUARY 10th

TODAY'S THOUGHT: "Never try to impress a woman, because if you do she'll expect you to keep up to the standard for the rest of your life." —*W.C. Fields*

HISTORY: On this date in 1897 the "New York Times" introduced its slogan, "All The News That's Fit To Print".

QUIZ: February is the second month. Can you name these two other seconds?
A: Paris is the largest French speaking city in the world. Which city is second?
B: John Hancock was the first to sign the Declaration of Independence. Who was second?

Trivia

Two states are the most "neighborly" of all; Missouri and Tennessee both touch on eight other states.

QUIZ ANSWER: A — Montreal; B — Samuel Adams

FEBRUARY 11th

TODAY'S THOUGHT: "You can only hold your stomach in for so many years." —*Burt Reynolds*

HISTORY: On this date in 1960 Jack Paar walked off his show in protest of the network's censoring of a mild "water closet" gag he had done the night before. After almost a month of negotiations, the show was back up to "Paar" as the host returned to his post.

QUIZ: Before he got into steamy novels of lust and lies, what sixties sitcoms did Sidney Sheldon create and write?

Trivia
In his lifetime Thomas Edison patented 1,093 inventions.

QUIZ ANSWER: He dreamed up "I Dream of Jeannie" and saw double with "The Patty Duke Show".

FEBRUARY 12th

TODAY'S THOUGHT: "My theory of evolution? I think Darwin was adopted." —*Steven Wright*

HISTORY: On this date in 1809 Abraham Lincoln was born.

QUIZ: Another of the greatest men of the 19th century was born today, the exact same day as Lincoln, half a world away. Any guesses?

Trivia
The word "caper" appeared in every episode title of "77 Sunset Strip".

QUIZ ANSWER: Charles Darwin — While Abe was destined to deal with revolution, Charles worked out evolution.

FEBRUARY 13th

TODAY'S THOUGHT: "Never slap a man who chews tobacco." —*Willard Scott*

HISTORY: On this date in 1741 the first American magazine, appropriately titled "The American Magazine", was published by Andrew Bradford.

QUIZ: Can you identify the following famous folks by their given names?

A: Joe Yule, Jr.   C: Michael Douglas
B: Walter Palahnuik   D: Mary Cathleen Collins

Trivia

Alice Kramden was known as Alice Gibson before she married Ralph.

QUIZ ANSWER: A — Mickey Rooney; B — Jack Palance; C — Michael Keaton; D — Bo Derek

FEBRUARY 14th

TODAY'S THOUGHT: "Never sign a valentine with your own name." —*Charles Dickens*

HISTORY: On this date in 1849 President James Polk became the first U.S. president to be photographed while in office.

QUIZ: How many pennies are in a pound?

A: 54   B: 100   C: 123   D: 181

Trivia

The post office in Loveland, Colorado is very busy today. It handles about 200,000 valentines every year.

QUIZ ANSWER: D — Were you "penny-wise" or "pound-foolish"?

FEBRUARY 15th

TODAY'S THOUGHT: "Middle age is when your old classmates are so grey and wrinkled and bald they don't recognize you." —*Bennett Cerf*

HISTORY: On this date in 1903 the first Teddy Bear made its appearance.

QUIZ: Famous Last Words: The quotes below were the last ever heard from the lips of the following people. Can you match them up?

1. "I have a terrible headache." A: Douglas Fairbanks, Sr.
2. "Strike my tent." B: Franklin D. Roosevelt
3. "I've never felt better." C: Robert E. Lee

Trivia
Disney World is twice the size of Manhattan.

QUIZ ANSWER: 1 — B; 2 — C; 3 — A

FEBRUARY 16th

TODAY'S THOUGHT: "Tennis is like marrying for money. Love has nothing to do with it." —*Phyllis Diller*

HISTORY: On this date in 1883 the very first issue of "The Ladies Home Journal" hit the newsstands. No doubt most of the coupons have expired by now.

QUIZ: Bathroom Brain Teaser: If your doctor gave you three pills and told you to take one every half hour, how long would they last?

Trivia
The microwave oven is used more for reheating coffee than for any other reason.

QUIZ ANSWER: One hour

FEBRUARY 17th

TODAY'S THOUGHT: "In spite of the cost of living, it's still popular." —*Kathleen Norris*

HISTORY: On this date in 1867 the first ship passed through the Suez Canal. In honor of the occasion the band was playing "Is Suez or is Su-ain't my baby?" So it's a horrible pun - so Suez!

QUIZ: Who are Moses Horwitz, Jerome Horwitz and Larry Feinberg?

Trivia
88 out of 100 people put on their right shoe first.

QUIZ ANSWER: They are the three Stooges: Moe, Curley and Larry.

FEBRUARY 18th

TODAY'S THOUGHT: "It's not the most intellectual job in the world, but I do have to know the letters."
—*Vanna White*

HISTORY: On this date in 1930 Pluto was discovered. He was sitting on a stool at Schwab's when Walt Disney came in...actually it was the planet Pluto, the smallest, farthest and coldest in the solar system.

QUIZ: True or False? Prince Charles is an avid collector of toilet seats.

Trivia
1 billion days is more than 2.7 million years.

QUIZ ANSWER: True

FEBRUARY 19th

TODAY'S THOUGHT: "A tourist is a fellow who drives thousands of miles so he can be photographed standing in front of his car." —*Emile Ganest*

HISTORY: On this date in 1884 the phonograph was patented and the phrase "Turn that down or you're grounded!" entered the language.

QUIZ: Which state has the longest coastline?

Trivia
Since 1912 more than 16 million toys have been given away in Cracker Jack boxes.

QUIZ ANSWER: By far, the state with the longest coastline is Alaska. In fact, its coastline is longer than that of all the other coastal states combined! Strange that it never became a beach resort...

FEBRUARY 20th

TODAY'S THOUGHT: "Work banishes those three great evils — boredom, vice and poverty." —*Voltaire*

HISTORY: On this date in 1962 Lt. Colonel John Glenn became the first American in orbit as he circled the earth three times in Friendship 7.

QUIZ: Here's a double extra super killer trivia question for you just to shake the cobwebs off your cranium: What is Donald Duck's middle name?

Trivia
Mickey Mouse's nephews are Morty and Ferdy.

QUIZ ANSWER: Fauntleroy

FEBRUARY 21st

TODAY'S THOUGHT: "If a man watches three football games in a row, he should be declared legally dead."
—Erma Bombeck

HISTORY: On this date in 1855 Lucy Hobbs became the first female to graduate from dental school in Cincinnati, Ohio. But since "Women's Lib" was more than a hundred years off, building a practice for Lucy was like pulling teeth...

QUIZ: What "first" do baseball luminaries Babe Ruth, Sparky Anderson and Tom Seaver share?

Trivia
A dog's nose print is as individual as a person's fingerprint.

QUIZ ANSWER: The same first name — George

FEBRUARY 22nd

TODAY'S THOUGHT: "Frankly, I don't mind not being president. I just mind that someone else is."
—Edward M. Kennedy

HISTORY: On this date in 1879 Franklin W. Woolworth opened his first five-and-ten cent store in Utica, New York.

QUIZ: Who was the originator of the military decoration known as "The Purple Heart"?

Trivia
The only state in the United States to be named after a president is Washington.

QUIZ ANSWER: It was originated by none other than George Washington. Since he often soaked his false teeth in wine, he created a special decoration for the army dentists who gave him that advice: the purple tooth.

FEBRUARY 23rd

TODAY'S THOUGHT: "Many a man owes his success to his first wife and his second to his success."
—*Jim Backus*

HISTORY: On this date in 1945 the U.S. flag was raised on Mt. Surabacki on Iwo Jima.

QUIZ: What is the only number spelled with the exact number of letters it stands for? And what number would you have to count up to in order to use all five vowels?

Trivia
Instead of letters, the Chinese have a different character for every single word.

QUIZ ANSWER: Four and one thousand

FEBRUARY 24th

TODAY'S THOUGHT: "Interest your kids in bowling. Get them off the streets and into the alleys."
—*Don Rickles*

HISTORY: On this date in 1980 the U.S. Hockey team won the gold medal at the Winter Olympics.

QUIZ: Which word is mispelled - parallel, embarrass, assassin?

Trivia
Hockey superstar Wayne Gretzky and former Los Angeles Kings owner Bruce McNall teamed up in 1991 to buy a Honus Wagner baseball card — for $451,000!

QUIZ ANSWER: You didn't fall for this, did you? "Mispelled" was misspelled.

FEBRUARY 25th

TODAY'S THOUGHT: "As far as I'm concerned, there won't be a Beatles reunion as long as John Lennon remains dead." —*George Harrison*

HISTORY: On this date in 1836 government officials issued the patent for the Colt revolver.

QUIZ: True or False?
A: Ships travel faster in cold water than warm.
B: Attila the Hun dropped dead on his wedding night.
C: The Oscar winning sci-fi film "Forbidden Planet" was based on a Shakespearean play.

Trivia
Honorificabilitudinitatibus is the longest word in the works of William Shakespeare.

QUIZ ANSWER: Believe it or not, they are all true.

FEBRUARY 26th

TODAY'S THOUGHT: "Thin people are beautiful but fat people are adorable." —*Jackie Gleason*

HISTORY: On this date in 1881 the S.S. Ceylon sailed from Liverpool, England on the very first around-the-world cruise.

QUIZ: In Britain the game is called "draughts". What is it called in the U.S.A.?

Trivia
The only one of the seven dwarfs who's beardless is Dopey.

QUIZ ANSWER: Checkers

FEBRUARY 27th

TODAY'S THOUGHT: "Success is a great deodorant. It takes away all your past smells." —*Elizabeth Taylor*

HISTORY: On this date in 1883 Oscar Hammerstein obtained a patent for the first cigar rolling machine. By the way, it was Oscar Hammerstein II who rolled out the lyrics for Richard Rodgers' music.

QUIZ: What was the original purpose of cuffs on men's trousers?

Trivia

The world's largest manufacturer of feminine apparel is Mattel, the toymaker. The company sells about twenty million Barbie doll costumes annually.

QUIZ ANSWER: They were originally added to catch cigar ashes.

FEBRUARY 28th

TODAY'S THOUGHT: "I don't jog. It makes the ice jump right out of my glass." —*Martin Mull*

HISTORY: On this date in 1983 Hawkeye Pierce, B.J. Hunnicut and the rest of the 4077 struck their tents and hit the road in the final episode of "M*A*S*H". It registered one of the highest ratings ever as 77 out of 100 people watching TV at the time tuned in.

QUIZ: What does M*A*S*H stand for?

Trivia

The first drive-in theater was opened in 1932 in Camden, New Jersey.

QUIZ ANSWER: Mobile Army Surgical Hospital

FEBRUARY 29th

TODAY'S THOUGHT: "Be yourself is the worst advice you can possibly give some people." —*Tom Masson*

HISTORY: On this date in 1904, the very first February 29th of the twentieth century, President Theodore Roosevelt appointed the Panama Canal Commission.

QUIZ: True or False? There is a town called Leap, Oregon which was named in a leap year.

Trivia

The oldest tree ever was a bristlecone pine found in eastern Nevada. When it was cut down, it was estimated to be 5,100 years old.

QUIZ ANSWER: True

MARCH 1st

TODAY'S THOUGHT: "Never eat more than you can lift."
—*Miss Piggy*

HISTORY: On this date in 1961 John F. Kennedy established the Peace Corps.

QUIZ: On the TV show "Green Acres", why did they replace Arnold the Pig?

Trivia
Austria was the first country to send postcards.

QUIZ ANSWER: Arnold, the second or third hammiest actor on "Green Acres", was secretly switched when he became too fat!

MARCH 2nd

TODAY'S THOUGHT: "Nothing in life is 'fun for the whole family'." —*Jerry Seinfeld*

HISTORY: On this date in 1836 Texas declared its independence from Mexico.

QUIZ: Bathroom Brain Teaser: John Smith was eight years old on his first birthday. How is that?

Trivia
A rockoon is a rocket and balloon hybrid used by weathermen to launch measuring instruments sixty miles high.

QUIZ ANSWER: He was born on February 29, 1896. The year 1900 was not a leap year (only centuries divisible by 400 are leap years) so Smith's first birthday was in 1904.

MARCH 3rd

TODAY'S THOUGHT: "Television is more interesting than people. If it were not, we should have people standing in the corners of our rooms." —*Alan Coren*

HISTORY: On this date in 1634 the first tavern in Boston opened its doors and its taps...a guy in a tri-cornered hat named Norm claimed the corner stool.

QUIZ: On the sitcom "Cheers", when was "Mayday" Malone Rookie of the Year?

Trivia

Giraffes make it necessary for the telephone poles in Kenya and Uganda to be much higher than those to which we are accustomed.

QUIZ ANSWER: Of course only a true connoisseur would know that Sam was Rookie of the Year in 1972.

MARCH 4th

TODAY'S THOUGHT: "Diplomacy is the art of saying 'Nice doggie' until you can find a rock." —*Will Rogers*

HISTORY: On this date in 1952 Ronald Reagan married Nancy Davis.

QUIZ: What state capital is the southernmost among the 48 contiguous states?

Trivia

Washington, D.C. has the highest ratio of lawyers per resident: 1 for every 19 people.

QUIZ ANSWER: Austin, Texas

MARCH 5th

TODAY'S THOUGHT: "I like a woman with a head on her shoulders. I hate necks." —*Steve Martin*

HISTORY: On this date in 1953 Soviet premier Joseph Stalin died in Moscow. His funeral was one of the largest affairs in Russian history.

QUIZ: Who was Sherlock Holmes named after? Actually, it's elementary, my dear Watson...

Trivia

There is no word in the English language which rhymes with purple.

QUIZ ANSWER: Sir Arthur Conan Doyle borrowed the name of his favorite American poet, Oliver Wendell Holmes.

MARCH 6th

TODAY'S THOUGHT: "The trouble with children is that they are not returnable." —*Quentin Crisp*

HISTORY: On this date in 1930 Clarence Birdseye put the first individually packaged frozen foods on sale — mothers throughout the country rejoiced.

QUIZ: What was the largest volcanic eruption in recorded history?

Trivia

During a single storm, the Empire State Building may be struck by lightning twenty times.

QUIZ ANSWER: If you said Mt. St. Helens, you aren't even close. That was a comparative firecracker compared to the eruption of Mt. Tambora which blew 220 million tons of dust and ash into the stratosphere in 1815, causing the "year without a summer".

MARCH 7th

TODAY'S THOUGHT: "A nickel ain't worth a dime anymore." —*Yogi Berra*

HISTORY: On this date in 1897 the first bowl of corn flakes was served by Dr. John Kellogg to one of his patients at a mental hospital in Battle Creek, Michigan.

QUIZ: Bathroom Brain Teaser: Suppose that 14% of the people in Detroit, Michigan have unlisted telephone numbers. Now suppose you randomly pick two hundred names from the phone book for that city. Assuming that the 14% figure holds true, how many of those names you've selected will have unlisted numbers?

Trivia
Little Lulu's last name was Moppet.

QUIZ ANSWER: None will be unlisted.

MARCH 8th

TODAY'S THOUGHT: "Being a living legend is better than being a dead legend." —*George Burns*

HISTORY: On this date in 1894 bureaucracy caught up to man's best friend as New York City passed its first dog licensing law.

QUIZ: Time for a little Monkee business: What TV show did Mickey Dolenz star in before he joined up with Peter, Mike and Davy?

Trivia
Eleven dogs played "Lassie" in the movie and TV series. Only one was female.

QUIZ ANSWER: As a child actor working under the name of Mickey Braddock, he starred in "Circus Boy".

MARCH 9th

TODAY'S THOUGHT: "I don't like to watch golf on television. I can't stand whispering." —*David Brenner*

HISTORY: On this date in 1822 the first U.S. patent for artificial teeth was issued to Charles Graham of New York City.

QUIZ: What is the average life expectancy of a one dollar bill?

A: 2 years   B: 9 months   C: 5 years   D: 1-1/2 years

Trivia

The name James Ritty should ring a bell — he invented the cash register in 1884.

QUIZ ANSWER: D — Not only doesn't a dollar go as far as it used to, it doesn't last as long as it used to.

MARCH 10th

TODAY'S THOUGHT: "Sports do not build character. They reveal it." —*Heywood Broun*

HISTORY: On this date in 1876 Alexander Graham Bell transmitted the very first telephone call to his assistant, Mr. Watson.

QUIZ: What do the following celebrities have in common: Mel Allen, Hoagy Carmichael, John Cleese, Howard Cosell, Julio Iglesias, Ozzie Nelson and Geraldo Rivera?

Trivia

Roy Rogers is the only person ever elected to the Country Music Hall of Fame twice.

QUIZ ANSWER: At one time they were all lawyers, but early in their careers decided to go straight.

MARCH 11th

TODAY'S THOUGHT: "Is sloppiness in speech caused by ignorance or apathy? I don't know and I don't care."
—*William Safire*

HISTORY: On this date in 1888 the "Blizzard of '88" struck the northeast and became the greatest storm of the century.

QUIZ: What hugely popular book took ten years to write and was the only one ever completed by its author?

Trivia
"Calcutta" was Lawrence Welk's only number one hit record, topping the charts in 1961.

QUIZ ANSWER: "Gone With The Wind" was the famous novel by Margaret Mitchell.

MARCH 12th

TODAY'S THOUGHT: "A gold rush is what happens when a line of chorus girls spot a man with a bank roll."
—*Mae West*

HISTORY: On this date in 1912 Juliet Low earned some big time brownie points as she organized the first Girl Scout troop in Savannah, Georgia.

QUIZ: AuH_2O was a popular bumper sticker for which 1960's U.S. presidential candidate?

Trivia
The strawberry is a member of the rose family.

QUIZ ANSWER: Barry Goldwater (Au is the chemical symbol for gold and H_2O is, of course, water.)

MARCH 13th

TODAY'S THOUGHT: "An economic downturn is when they don't have money. A recession is when you don't have money and a depression is when I don't have money." —*Sanford Mims*

HISTORY: On this date in 1852 "Uncle Sam" was born in an editorial cartoon in the New York "Lantern". The character was based on an officer from the War of 1812, Sam Wilson.

QUIZ: How many calories does one Hershey's Kisses chocolate contain?

> **Trivia**
> *Venetian blinds were invented by the Chinese.*

QUIZ ANSWER: 25 calories

MARCH 14th

TODAY'S THOUGHT: "If I had my life to live over again, I'd be a plumber." —*Albert Einstein*

HISTORY: On this date in 1923 Warren G. Harding became the first president to file an income tax.

QUIZ: What is comedian Albert Brooks' real name?

> **Trivia**
> *Sources say that Albert Einstein never wore socks.*

QUIZ ANSWER: He was born Albert Einstein. His brother is Bob Einstein, Officer Judy of the old "Smothers Brothers' Comedy Hour", who nowadays wears a crash helmet as Super Dave Osborne. Brooks' father, Harry, was a famous radio comedian whom old-timers may remember as Parkyakarkas.

MARCH 15th

TODAY'S THOUGHT: "One man with courage makes a majority." —*Andrew Jackson*

HISTORY: On this date in 44 B.C. Julius Caesar was told to "beware the Ides of March". He must not have kept his ides open as he was assassinated.

QUIZ: What do a.m. and p.m. stand for, anyway?

Trivia

The White House was originally grey. It was burned during the War of 1812 and later rebuilt and painted white to cover the smoke stains.

QUIZ ANSWER: "Ante meridiem", Latin for "before noon" and "post meridiem" for "after noon" —The custom of beginning days at midnight rather than at sunset comes to us from the Romans.

MARCH 16th

TODAY'S THOUGHT: "The trouble with the average family is it has too much month left over at the end of the money." —*Bill Vaughan*

HISTORY: On this date in 1802 West Point Military Academy in New York was established by an Act of Congress.

QUIZ: Jackie Robinson was the first African-American big league baseball player. Who was the second?

Trivia

Pink lemonade was created in 1857 by Pete Conklin who unwittingly used a bucket of water in which a circus performer had soaked his red tights.

QUIZ ANSWER: Larry Doby

MARCH 17th

TODAY'S THOUGHT: "We have always found the Irish a bit odd. They refuse to be English." —*Winston Churchill*

HISTORY: On this date in 1845 the rubber band was invented.

QUIZ: What nocturnal "first" do Groucho Marx, Tony Bennett, Mel Brooks, Rudy Vallee and Joan Crawford have in common?

Trivia

All Japanese words end in vowels or the letter "n".

QUIZ ANSWER: They were the guest lineup the night Johnny Carson took over the "Tonight Show" on October 1, 1962.

MARCH 18th

TODAY'S THOUGHT: "I told my mother-in-law that my house was her house, and she said, 'Get the hell off my property.'" —*Joan Rivers*

HISTORY: On this date in 1931 the electric razor was first marketed by Schick.

QUIZ: From which show in the late sixties was "Happy Days" a spinoff?

Trivia

The most common name for a town in the United States is Fairview.

QUIZ ANSWER: "Happy Days" began as a segment on the lighthearted romance anthology "Love, American Style" and then spun off "Laverne and Shirley", "Mork and Mindy" and "Joanie Loves Chachie".

MARCH 19th

TODAY'S THOUGHT: "I hate women because they always know where things are." —*James Thurber*

HISTORY: On this date in 1931 we bet you didn't know that Nevada legalized gambling.

QUIZ: The last name is Buonarroti. What's the first name?

A: Madonna   B: Michelangelo   C: (Tiny) Tim
D: Favio

Trivia

A duck has three eyelids. That way he can open it just a quack!

QUIZ ANSWER: B

MARCH 20th

TODAY'S THOUGHT: "The reason lightning doesn't strike twice in the same place is that the same place isn't there the second time." —*Willie Tyler*

HISTORY: On this date in 1859 "Uncle Tom's Cabin", by Harriet Beecher Stowe, was published.

QUIZ: Who am I? I'm a bird that can't fly. I'm eight feet tall. I live and work and play in New York City. My street address is 123-1/2. And, although I am ageless, today is my birthday.

Trivia

The first newspaper crossword puzzle, by Arthur Wynne, appeared in the "New York World" on December 21, 1913.

QUIZ ANSWER: Big Bird from "Sesame Street"

MARCH 21st

TODAY'S THOUGHT: "A lawyer is a gentleman who rescues your estate from your enemies and keeps it for himself." —*Lord Brougham*

HISTORY: On this date in 1891 a Hatfield and a McCoy were married, ending a lengthy West Virginia feud. Watch for them on the next episode of "Family Feud"!

QUIZ: Bathroom Brain Teaser: The man married the little boy's mother, but was not his father (in any step of the way). Who was he?

Trivia

Borborygmus is the technical term for a growling stomach.

QUIZ ANSWER: The clergyman

MARCH 22nd

TODAY'S THOUGHT: "You don't want no pie in the sky when you die, You want something here on the ground while you're still around." —*Muhammad Ali*

HISTORY: On this date in 1967 Muhammad Ali was stripped of his heavyweight title by the World Boxing Association for refusing military induction.

QUIZ: When is the birthday of "Star Trek's" Captain James T. Kirk?

Trivia

Three out of four Americans like to doodle.

QUIZ ANSWER: You just missed it — March 21st. Wait! Before running out to pick up a belated birthday card, cool your jets. The future captain of the USS Enterprise won't be born until the year 2228. Riverside, Iowa claims to be his future birthplace.

MARCH 23rd

TODAY'S THOUGHT: "Health nuts are going to feel stupid someday, lying in hospitals dying of nothing."
—*Redd Foxx*

HISTORY: On this date in 1775 Patrick Henry gave his "Give Me Liberty Or Give Me Death" speech. Henry was a happy man... eventually he got both.

QUIZ: What is the abbreviation "Mrs." short for?

Trivia
The act of snapping your fingers is called "fillip".

QUIZ ANSWER: Actually, it's not really an abbreviation at all because it can't be written out as a complete word. Long ago, it was short for mistress, but not anymore.

MARCH 24th

TODAY'S THOUGHT: "A committee is a group that keeps minutes and loses hours." —*Milton Berle*

HISTORY: On this date in 1958 Elvis got his sideburns chopped and his head shaved as he gave a two year command performance for Uncle Sam.

QUIZ: Harry Houdini, born on this date, made his final disappearing act in strangely coincidental fashion. Do you know the day Houdini died?

Trivia
T.S. Eliot's initials stand for Thomas Stearns.

QUIZ ANSWER: On Halloween in 1926

MARCH 25th

TODAY'S THOUGHT: "Sports is the toy department of human life." *—Howard Cosell*

HISTORY: On this date in 1954 the NBC peacock got a feather in its cap when RCA began manufacturing color television sets.

QUIZ: What does a pogonophobic fear?

Trivia

Mount Rushmore's rock stars are George Washington, Thomas Jefferson, Theodore Roosevelt and Abraham Lincoln.

QUIZ ANSWER: A pogonophobic finds beards to be a hair-raising experience.

MARCH 26th

TODAY'S THOUGHT: "The trouble with unemployment is that the minute you wake up in the morning you're on the job." *—Slappy White*

HISTORY: On this date in 1953 Dr. Jonas Salk announced a new vaccine to immunize against polio.

QUIZ: What is the name of the little man with the top hat and mustache in the game of Monopoly?

A: Daddy Warbucks   B: I.M. Rich   C: Mr. Monopoly
D: Rich Uncle Pennybags

Trivia

Four out of five people who try out a new pen will write their own name.

QUIZ ANSWER: D — Uncle Pennybags must be rich indeed. Parker Brothers has sold well over 100 million Monopoly games since its introduction in 1933.

MARCH 27th

TODAY'S THOUGHT: "Why is there always a mailbox in front of the post office?" —*Gallagher*

HISTORY: On this date in 1917 the U.S. wrested the Stanley Cup from the Canadians for the first time as the Seattle Metropolitans defeated the Montreal Canadians.

QUIZ: What do approximately one million people drink as their beverage of choice at breakfast each day?

Trivia
The average person spends five years of their precious time on Earth waiting on lines.

QUIZ ANSWER: Coke is it! The company estimates that about $237 million of the Real Thing is guzzled at breakfast every year.

MARCH 28th

TODAY'S THOUGHT: "This would be a better world for children if parents had to eat the spinach."
—*Groucho Marx*

HISTORY: On this date in 1979 Three Mile Island, a reactor complex near Harrisburg, Pennsylvania blew its cool and came close to a core meltdown.

QUIZ: How many bones does a shark have?

Trivia
The story most often made into a movie is "Cinderella", no less than 58 times.

QUIZ ANSWER: 0

MARCH 29th

TODAY'S THOUGHT: "There is only one boss. The customer. And he can fire everybody in the company from the chairman on down, simply by spending his money somewhere else." —*Sam Walton*

HISTORY: On this date in 1848 an ice jam formed in Lake Erie that was so bad Niagara Falls actually ran dry for a full day.

QUIZ: What is the most commonly used word in the English language?

Trivia
A pullicologist is an expert of fleas.

QUIZ ANSWER: Of the I sing — The most commonly used word is "the".

MARCH 30th

TODAY'S THOUGHT: "I dream my painting and then I paint my dream." —*Vincent Van Gogh*

HISTORY: On this date in 1858 Philadelphian Hyman Lippman patented the first pencil with an attached eraser.

QUIZ: When "Rolling Stone" premiered back in 1967, what familiar face graced the cover of the first issue?

Trivia
If the coils of the French horn were straightened out, the instrument would be 22 feet long.

QUIZ ANSWER: Although many famous faces have appeared on the cover of "Rolling Stone", John Lennon's was the first.

MARCH 31st

TODAY'S THOUGHT: "We should be grateful for subways. At least they've taken crime off the street."
—*Will Jordan*

HISTORY: On this date in 1889 the Eiffel Tower opened for business in Paris.

QUIZ: This inventor was one of the original founders of "National Geographic". Using the pen name H.A. Largelamb, he also wrote for the magazine. His real name ought to ring a bell. Do you know it?

Trivia
Tuesday Weld was born on a Friday.

QUIZ ANSWER: Alexander Graham Bell —
(H.A. Largelamb unscrambled is A. Graham Bell.)

APRIL 1st

TODAY'S THOUGHT: "The better I get to know men, the more I find myself loving dogs." —*Charles De Gaulle*

HISTORY: On this date in 1889 Mrs. W.A. Cockran of Shelbyville, Indiana perfected the first dishwasher which was marketed in Chicago.

QUIZ: Dogs That Do It On The Funny Papers...
See if you can name the pooches from the following comic strips:

"Peanuts"   "Dennis the Menace"   "Blondie"

Trivia

Splinter and Knothead were Woody Woodpecker's niece and nephew.

QUIZ ANSWER: In "Peanuts" it is Snoopy; "Dennis the Menace" owns Ruff; and "Blondie" pets Daisy.

APRIL 2nd

TODAY'S THOUGHT: "Never go to a doctor whose office plants have died." —*Erma Bombeck*

HISTORY: On this date in 1792 Congress established the United States Mint in Philadelphia.

QUIZ: Four U.S. state capitals are named after presidents. How many can you name?

Trivia

Fairy tale writer Hans Christian Andersen was dyslexic. Others afflicted by dyslexia include Thomas Edison, Woodrow Wilson, Tom Cruise and Henry Winkler.

QUIZ ANSWER: Jackson, Mississippi; Jefferson City, Missouri; Lincoln, Nebraska; Madison, Wisconsin

APRIL 3rd

TODAY'S THOUGHT: "When you become senile, you won't know it." —*Bill Cosby*

HISTORY: On this date in 1860 the first Pony Express began. It hightailed between Sacramento, California and St. Joseph, Missouri.

QUIZ: How is it determined on what date Easter will occur in any given year?

Trivia
The official state beverage of Massachusetts is cranberry juice.

QUIZ ANSWER: It is tied to the lunar cycle. Easter is the first Sunday after the first full moon after the vernal equinox.

APRIL 4th

TODAY'S THOUGHT: "Man is the only animal, I believe, who pretends he is thinking of other things while he is eating." —*Robert Lynd*

HISTORY: On this date in 1968 Martin Luther King Jr. was assassinated in Memphis, Tennessee by James Earl Ray.

QUIZ: Everyone knows that February is the shortest month but what is the second shortest month?

Trivia
An ostrich can cover 25 feet in a single stride.

QUIZ ANSWER: April is the second shortest month. It has only thirty days which puts it in a tie with June, September and November. The tie breaker is the fact that Daylight Savings Time cuts an extra hour out of April.

APRIL 5th

TODAY'S THOUGHT: "Where lipstick is concerned, the important thing is not the color, but to accept God's final decision on where your lips end." —*Jerry Seinfeld*

HISTORY: On this date in 1614 John Rolfe and Pocahontas were married in Virginia.

QUIZ: Seventies Flashback: Who was Melvin Dummar and for what did he become briefly famous in the seventies?

Trivia
In the days of King Henry VIII, knitting was the specialty of men, not women.

QUIZ ANSWER: Dummar was a gas station attendant in Willard, Utah who claimed that Howard Hughes had left his fortune to him.

APRIL 6th

TODAY'S THOUGHT: "The scientific theory I like best is that the rings of Saturn are composed entirely of lost airline luggage." —*Mark Russell*

HISTORY: On this date in 1896 the first modern Olympic Games began in Athens, Greece.

QUIZ: In the film "The Natural", what is the name of Robert Redford's team?

Trivia
Zip-a-dee-doo-dah: To bankers, ZIP is an acronym for Zero Interest Payment; to psychologists, ZIP is short for Zero Intelligence Potential; to postal workers, ZIP stands for Zone Improvement Plan.

QUIZ ANSWER: Redford was a Johnny-come-lately player for the New York Knights.

APRIL 7th

TODAY'S THOUGHT: "Vote Labor and you build castles in the air. Vote Conservative and you can live in them." —*David Frost*

HISTORY: On this date in 1868 Mormon Church leader Brigham Young married his 27th (and final) wife.

QUIZ: True or False? Napoleon Bonaparte, a Frenchman, designed the flag of Italy.

Trivia
There is a club in the United States whose only membership requirement is that your name is Jim Smith. At last count there were 781 members.

QUIZ ANSWER: True

APRIL 8th

TODAY'S THOUGHT: "A verbal contract isn't worth the paper it's written on." —*Samuel Goldwyn*

HISTORY: On this date in 1974 Hammerin' Hank Aaron of the Atlanta Braves broke Babe Ruth's home run record, hitting his 715th lifetime round tripper in a game against the Los Angeles Dodgers.

QUIZ: Bathroom Brain Teaser: There are ten black socks and ten white socks in a drawer. If you reach into the drawer in the dark, how many socks must you take out in order to know that you have a matching pair?

Trivia
A penguin is the only bird that can swim but not fly.

QUIZ ANSWER: Three — All three will be the same color, or two will be one color and the third will be the other color.

APRIL 9th

TODAY'S THOUGHT: "If three-fourths of the earth's surface is covered with water, how come it's so hard to get to the beach?" —*Teresa Skelton*

HISTORY: On this date in 1953 the first issue of "TV Guide" was published.

QUIZ: Dr. Benjamin Spock, American child care guru, achieved quite a distinction in sports in his youth. Any idea what it was?

Trivia

While married, Sonny and Cher sometimes communicated by writing to each other in a diary — left in their bathroom.

QUIZ ANSWER: Strangely enough, the great opponent of paddling was a member of the American Rowing Gold Medal Team in the 1924 Paris Olympics.

APRIL 10th

TODAY'S THOUGHT: "Why torture yourself when life will do it for you?" —*Laura Walker*

HISTORY: On this date in 1912 the "unsinkable" Titanic set sail on her ill-fated voyage.

QUIZ: Which of the following is false regarding the kangaroo?

A: If you hold a kangaroo by its tail, it cannot jump.
B: A group of kangaroos is known as a mob.
C: The leader of a group is referred to as the captain kangaroo.

Trivia

1 Cherry Street in New York City was home to George Washington as it was the first U.S. presidential address.

QUIZ ANSWER: C (Yes, this was a gimme, Mate.)

APRIL 11th

TODAY'S THOUGHT: "The trouble with life in the fast lane is that you get to the other end in an awful hurry."
—*John Jensen*

HISTORY: On this date in 1814 Napoleon Bonaparte was abdicated as Emperor of France and banished to the island of Elba.

QUIZ: By what nickname did the world know Robert Stroud?

Trivia

The Bronx is the only part of New York City connected to the mainland.

QUIZ ANSWER: One of the most famous residents of "The Rock", Stroud was known as "The Birdman of Alcatraz".

APRIL 12th

TODAY'S THOUGHT: "Be suspicious of any doctor who tries to take your temperature with his finger."
—*David Letterman*

HISTORY: On this date in 1861 Confederates fired on Fort Sumter in Charleston harbor, touching off the Civil War.

QUIZ: What kind of people have never appeared in the comic strip "Peanuts"?

Trivia

Tombstones were originally placed on plots over the dead so that the deceased could not come out and harm the living.

QUIZ ANSWER: The strip definitely discriminates against adults. None have ever appeared with Charlie Brown and company.

APRIL 13th

TODAY'S THOUGHT: "Swearing was invented as a compromise between running away and fighting."
—Finley Peter Dunne

HISTORY: On this date in 1976 the United States Mint reissued the $2 bill with the likeness of Thomas Jefferson.

QUIZ: Jerry Lee Lewis, Liberace and Van Cliburn no doubt practiced this exercise written by Arthur de Lulli in 1877. What is it?

Trivia
Eight United States presidents have been born in Virginia.

QUIZ ANSWER: "Chopsticks"

APRIL 14th

TODAY'S THOUGHT: "What counts is not necessarily the size of the dog in the fight — it's the size of the fight in the dog." *—Dwight D. Eisenhower*

HISTORY: On this date in 1865 President Lincoln was shot by John Wilkes Booth at Ford's Theater.

QUIZ: What future president once played fourteen games as a minor league outfielder in Junction City, Kansas under an assumed name and piqued the interest of several major league scouts?

Trivia
There is a tribe of athletes in Burma called the Intha that row their longboats with their legs.

QUIZ ANSWER: Dwight David Eisenhower was this budding athlete.

APRIL 15th

TODAY'S THOUGHT: "Only little people pay taxes."
—*Leona Helmsley*

HISTORY: On this date in 1955 Ray Kroc opened his first McDonald's restaurant. The slogan at the time was "Q.S.C.V." (Quality, Service, Cleanliness and Value)

QUIZ: What is the tallest tree in the world?

Trivia
There are 119 grooves on the circumference of a quarter.

QUIZ ANSWER: You may be tempted to say Uncle Sam's Money Tree, but the tallest species is the coast redwood, the tallest example of which is in the Redwood Creek Grove, Humbolt County, California.
It measures 367.8 feet!

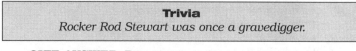

APRIL 16th

TODAY'S THOUGHT: "Comedy is simply a funny way of being serious." —*Peter Ustinov*

HISTORY: On this date in 1940 an event occurred which sparked the following brain teaser. The Cleveland Indians were playing the Chicago White Sox. No one on the White Sox got a hit. Yet none of their batting averages changed. Why not? The answer: It was opening day. Hall of Famer Bob Feller threw a no-hitter, the only no-hitter on opening day in baseball history.

QUIZ: What is the only way to tell a male penguin from a female penguin? (Assuming you're not a penguin)

Trivia
Rocker Rod Stewart was once a gravedigger.

QUIZ ANSWER: By autopsy

APRIL 17th

TODAY'S THOUGHT: "Some cause happiness wherever they go; others whenever they go." —*Oscar Wilde*

HISTORY: On this date in 1961 an invasion force halfheartedly backed by the United States was repelled at Cuba's Bay of Pigs.

QUIZ: Name at least three of the five actors who played Sgt. Friday's partners in "Dragnet".

Trivia
The average American has a 10,000 word vocabulary.

QUIZ ANSWER: Sure you guessed Harry Morgan, and maybe even Ben Alexander. But what about those other guys...Barton Yarborough, Herb Ellis and Barney Phillips.

APRIL 18th

TODAY'S THOUGHT: "My wife and I were happy for twenty years. Then we met." —*Rodney Dangerfield*

HISTORY: On this date in 1775 Paul Revere went on his legendary midnight ride to warn the countryside that "The British are coming!" Along with Revere rode William Dawes who never got credit despite the fact that Revere was captured early on, had his horse taken away from him and was sent packing back to Boston on foot, leaving Dawes to alert the patriots.

QUIZ: What was the game of Scrabble originally called?

Trivia
37% of Americans own dogs; 26% have cats in their household; 5% own birds.

QUIZ ANSWER: Lexico

APRIL 19th

TODAY'S THOUGHT: "Some luck lies in not getting what you thought you wanted but getting what you have, which once you have got it you may be smart enough to see is what you would have wanted had you known."
—*Garrison Keillor*

HISTORY: On this date in 1897 the first Boston marathon was run.

QUIZ: What was the largest denomination of United States currency ever minted?

Trivia

Julio Iglesias is so intensely superstitious that he'll leave a dinner table if salt is spilled. And if he hears really bad news, he'll remove all his clothing and dispose of it.

QUIZ ANSWER: A $100,000 bill which bore a portrait of Woodrow Wilson was the largest denomination.

APRIL 20th

TODAY'S THOUGHT: "The quizzical expression of the monkey at the zoo comes from his wondering whether he is his brother's keeper, or his keeper's brother."
—*Evan Esar*

HISTORY: On this date in 1589 in Angola, Andrew Battel became the first European to see a gorilla. He named the animal a "pongo".

QUIZ: In which hand does the Statue of Liberty hold her torch?

Trivia

When the mood of an octopus changes, so does its color.

QUIZ ANSWER: Right

APRIL 21st

TODAY'S THOUGHT: "Nature never makes any blunders; when she makes a fool, she means it."
—*Josh Billings*

HISTORY: On this date in 753 B.C., Rome was founded — even though it wasn't built in a day!

QUIZ: What was the name of the second baseman in Abbott and Costello's "Who's on First?" routine.

Trivia

In addition to inventing dynamite, Alfred Nobel was the pioneer of plywood.

QUIZ ANSWER: That's right. Look at the quiz and you'll note that it's a statement, not a question.

APRIL 22nd

TODAY'S THOUGHT: "The laziest man I ever met put popcorn in his pancakes so they would turn over by themselves." —*W.C. Fields*

HISTORY: On this date in 1864 the phrase "In God We Trust" was first added to United States coinage. One previous slogan printed on earlier coins was "Mind Your Business".

QUIZ: What do First Ladies Martha Washington, Abigail Fillmore, Caroline Harrison, Florence Harding and Pat Nixon have in common?

Trivia

Seventy percent of house dust is dead skin cells.

QUIZ ANSWER: They were all older than their husbands.

APRIL 23rd

TODAY'S THOUGHT: "Men get to be a mixture of the charming mannerisms of the women they have known."
—*F. Scott Fitzgerald*

HISTORY: On this date in 1896 the first public exhibition of moving pictures took place in New York City.

QUIZ: What was the significance of a character named Dippy Dawg in a 1932 Disney cartoon called "Mickey's Revue"?

Trivia

William Shakespeare was born on April 23 and died fifty-two years later on April 23.

QUIZ ANSWER: Dippy Dawg had not yet acquired the stage name, Goofy, that would carry him through over six decades of show-biz fame and fortune.

APRIL 24th

TODAY'S THOUGHT: "Never have children, only grandchildren." —*Gore Vidal*

HISTORY: On this date in 1888 Kodak sold its first camera.

QUIZ: What Apollo astronaut is the father of a soap star?

Trivia

"Kilroy was here" referred to James J. Kilroy, an inspector for Bethlehem Steel who used it as his certification mark.

QUIZ ANSWER: Michael Collins, left behind to pilot the command module while his shipmates Neil Armstrong and Edwin "Buzz" Aldrin made history by landing on the moon, is the father of Kate Collins who, for many years, has played Natalie on "All My Children".

APRIL 25th

TODAY'S THOUGHT: "Is fuel efficiency really what we need most desperately? I say what we really need is a car that can be shot when it breaks down."
—*Russell Baker*

HISTORY: On this date in 1901 New York became the first state to require license plates on cars.

QUIZ: Why should we remember Martin Waldseemuller?

Trivia
The first automobile to offer seat belts was the 1950 Nash.

QUIZ ANSWER: Simply put, Martin Waldseemuller is the guy who gave America its name. A German mapmaker and geographer, Waldseemuller was under the impression that Amerigo Vespucci had discovered the New World and so named the land in honor of him.

APRIL 26th

TODAY'S THOUGHT: "Adolescence is one big walking pimple." —*Carol Burnett*

HISTORY: On this date in 1986 the Chernobyl nuclear power plant exploded.

QUIZ: Can you identify the people who spoke these famous words?
A: "Ich bin ein Berliner!"
B: "Anyone who hates children and dogs can't be all bad."
C: "If you've seen one redwood tree, you've seen them all."

Trivia
Bookkeeper is the only word in the English language that has three consecutive sets of double letters.

QUIZ ANSWER: A — JFK; B — W.C. Fields;
C — Ronald Reagan

APRIL 27th

TODAY'S THOUGHT: "Stay humble. Always answer the phone — no matter who else is in the car."
—*Jack Lemmon*

HISTORY: On this date in 1897 U.S. Grant made a posthumous move to his permanent residence in Grant's Tomb, New York City.

QUIZ: Is the tomato a fruit or a vegetable?

Trivia
Samuel Morse actually made his living as a portrait painter.

QUIZ ANSWER: It is a case of you say "tomato" and I say "tomahto". Botanists classify the tomato as a fruit but the United States Supreme Court has settled the matter, legally ruling it a vegetable.

APRIL 28th

TODAY'S THOUGHT: "The reason there are two senators for every state is so that one can be the designated driver." —*Jay Leno*

HISTORY: On this date in 1789 the Mutiny on the Bounty occurred. Captain Bligh pulled off one of the most amazing feats of seamanship ever accomplished by sailing 3,600 miles in a small open boat back to civilization.

QUIZ: True or False? Only African elephants are trained.

Trivia
The only animal with four knees is the elephant.

QUIZ ANSWER: False, it is exactly the opposite. Only Indian elephants perform.

APRIL 29th

TODAY'S THOUGHT: "Don't be afraid to make a mistake; your readers might like it."
—*William Randolph Hearst*

HISTORY: On this date in 1553 the practice of using starch on linen was introduced by Mrs. Dingheim, a Flemish woman living in England.

QUIZ: Who is Frank Wills and what small but crucial role did he play in recent American history?

Trivia
The world's oldest gloves were found in King Tut's tomb and are over 3,300 years old.

QUIZ ANSWER: Wills was the twenty-four-year old security guard who discovered the Watergate break-in, the "third-rate burglary" that eventually toppled the Nixon administration.

APRIL 30th

TODAY'S THOUGHT: "A friend that ain't in need is a friend indeed." —*Kin Hubbard*

HISTORY: On this date in 1900 John Luther Jones, whose nickname came from his hometown of Cayce, Kentucky died while bravely staying at the controls of the Illinois Central railroad's Cannonball Express as it crashed into the caboose of a freight train, thereby inspiring many a legend and famous folk song.

QUIZ: Which two states have names that come from the Sioux word meaning "friend"?

Trivia
Robot comes from the Czech word for slave.

QUIZ ANSWER: North and South Dakota

MAY 1st

TODAY'S THOUGHT: "I came from a poor family. We never had meat at our house. And whenever I would go by a butcher's window I thought there had been a terrible accident." —*Jack Paar*

HISTORY: On this date in 1931 the Empire State Building was opened by President Hoover and Governor Smith.

QUIZ: What was the full name of Skipper on "Gilligan's Island"?

Trivia
The city of Hollywood was formerly known as Paradise Valley.

QUIZ ANSWER: Jonas Grunby

MAY 2nd

TODAY'S THOUGHT: "There are only two things a child will share willingly — communicable diseases and his mother's age." —*Dr. Benjamin Spock*

HISTORY: On this date in 1885 the first issue of "Good Housekeeping" cleaned up at the newsstands.

QUIZ: From the College of Trivial Knowledge: On what campus would you find the "Animal House"?

Trivia
Australia is the only continent without an active volcano.

QUIZ ANSWER: Faber College

MAY 3rd

TODAY'S THOUGHT: "For the parents of a Little Leaguer, a baseball game is simply a nervous breakdown into innings." —*Earl Wilson*

HISTORY: On this date in 1973 Chicago's Sears Tower, America's tallest building, opened for business.

QUIZ: Can you guess the famous names of the following folks?

A: Ellis McDaniel
B: Krekor Ohanian
C: Edward Bridge Danson III
D: Shelton Lee
E: Sarah Ophelia Colley Cannon

Trivia
The French poodle originated in Germany.

QUIZ ANSWER: A — Bo Diddley; B — Mike Connors; C — Ted Danson; D — Spike Lee; E — Minnie Pearl

MAY 4th

TODAY'S THOUGHT: "The temperature in any room is room temperature." —*Steven Wright*

HISTORY: On this date in 1961 Commander Alan B. Shepard Jr. sat atop a Redstone booster at Cape Canaveral and became the first American in space with his brief suborbital flight.

QUIZ: Who was brought in to dub Lauren Bacall's singing in "To Have and Have Not"?

Trivia
It is impossible to sneeze and keep your eyes open at the same time.

QUIZ ANSWER: A very young Andy Williams provided her with those velvety tones.

MAY 5th

TODAY'S THOUGHT: "I once wanted to become an atheist, but I gave up - they have no holidays."
—*Henny Youngman*

HISTORY: On this date in 1904 Cy Young pitched baseball's first perfect game.

QUIZ: Which of the following celebrities was not born in the city indicated?
A: Henny Youngman — Liverpool, England
B: Audrey Meadows — Wu Chang, China
C: Sid Caesar — Mexico City, Mexico

Trivia
A bowling ball outweighs a ping pong ball 2800 to 1.

QUIZ ANSWER: C — Sid Caesar was born in far-off, exotic Yonkers, New York.

MAY 6th

TODAY'S THOUGHT: "George Washington said to his father, 'If I never tell a lie, how can I get to be president?'" —*Red Buttons*

HISTORY: On this date in 1626 Peter Minuit bought Manhattan Island for $24.

QUIZ: Which of the following amazing facts is bogus?
A: During World War I sheep were employed to mow the grass at the White House.
B: Clark Gable had webbed feet.
C: Conductors live longer than average because of their regular upper body workouts.

Trivia
The average adult in the United States reads just 24 minutes a day.

QUIZ ANSWER: B—The King had normal tootsies.

MAY 7th

TODAY'S THOUGHT: "What a good thing Adam had — when he said a good thing, he knew nobody had said it before." —*Mark Twain*

HISTORY: On this date in 1915 the Lusitania went to the bottom after being torpedoed by a German U-boat.

QUIZ: Who was Chester Carlson and why did he and the Haloid Company make history?

Trivia

The motto of the FBI is "Fidelity, Bravery, Integrity".

QUIZ ANSWER: Carlson was an inventor with a new idea, the first xerographic copy, who was turned down by every major corporation including RCA and IBM. He finally sold his patents to the small Haloid Company which soon changed its name to Xerox.

MAY 8th

TODAY'S THOUGHT: "I have found the best way to give advice to your children is to find out what they want and then advise them to do it." —*Harry S Truman*

HISTORY: On this date in 1886 Dr. John Pemberton of Atlanta, Georgia invented Coca-Cola.

QUIZ: What does the S in Harry S Truman stand for?

Trivia

The president and vice-president of the United States are not allowed to travel together.

QUIZ ANSWER: The S was not an initial; it did not stand for anything.

MAY 9th

TODAY'S THOUGHT: "My uncle's funeral cost five thousand dollars so far. We buried him in a rented tuxedo." —*Dave Madden*

HISTORY: On this date in 1783 the first Purple Hearts were awarded to Sergeants Daniel Bissell, William Brown and Elijah Churchill.

QUIZ: What was the shortest month on record?

Trivia
Early watches had only one hand which indicated the hour.

QUIZ ANSWER: September, 1752 — During the switch from the Gregorian to the Julian calendar, eleven days were dropped from the month. That means absolutely nothing happened between September 3 and September 13 of that year.

MAY 10th

TODAY'S THOUGHT: "The hardest job kids face today is learning good manners without seeing any."
—*Fred Astaire*

HISTORY: On this date in 1869 the Golden Spike was driven in Promontory, Utah to complete the first transcontinental railroad.

QUIZ: Walt Disney received one big Oscar and seven small Oscars at the 1938 Academy Awards. What were they for?

Trivia
Fred Astaire was allergic to feathers.

QUIZ ANSWER: "Snow White and the Seven Dwarfs"

MAY 11th

TODAY'S THOUGHT: "Liberals feel unworthy of their posssessions. Conservatives feel they deserve everything they've stolen." —*Mort Sahl*

HISTORY: On this date in 1752 the first United States fire insurance policy was issued.

QUIZ: What is the only team in American pro sports to be named after an insect?

Trivia
The record for spitting a watermelon seed is 65 feet, 4 inches.

QUIZ ANSWER: The NBA's Charlotte Hornets

MAY 12th

TODAY'S THOUGHT: "You can observe a lot just by watching." —*Yogi Berra*

HISTORY: On this date in 1896 the New York City Department of Health passed a law prohibiting spitting.

QUIZ: What vegetable do you discard the outside, cook the inside, eat the outside and chuck the inside?

Trivia
There is a separate silk strand for each kernel on an ear of corn.

QUIZ ANSWER: Corn on the cob

MAY 13th

TODAY'S THOUGHT: "Have you ever noticed that mice don't have shoulders?" —*George Carlin*

HISTORY: On this date in 1950 the first Diner's Club credit card was issued.

QUIZ: In which mid-sixties movie did Stevie Wonder make his film debut?

Trivia
In 1915 the average annual American family income was $687.

QUIZ ANSWER: "Little" Stevie Wonder was in "Muscle Beach Party" with Frankie Avalon and Annette Funicello. He was such a hit they brought him back for "Bikini Beach".

MAY 14th

TODAY'S THOUGHT: "Gossip is the art of saying nothing in a way that leaves practically nothing unsaid."
—*Walter Winchell*

HISTORY: On this date in 1853 Gail Borden applied for a U.S. patent for his process for making condensed milk. His process turned out to be a cash cow as it was eventually marketed by a company called Borden.

QUIZ: Can you identify these behind the scenes voices?
A: Charlie from "Charlie's Angels"
B: The voice of God in the 1966 film, "The Bible"
C: The narrator of television's "Untouchables"

Trivia
Over 100 million Americans are on a diet on any given day.

QUIZ ANSWER: A — John Forsythe; B — John Huston, who also directed; C — Walter Winchell

MAY 15th

TODAY'S THOUGHT: "If your wife wants to learn to drive, don't stand in her way." —*Sam Levenson*

HISTORY: On this date in 1930 Ellen Church, the first "air hostess", greeted passengers aboard a United Airlines flight between California and Wyoming.

QUIZ: Where did author L. Frank Baum get the name for Oz, his magical land over the rainbow?

Trivia

The higher a plane flies, the less fuel it uses as the atmosphere is thinner and the vehicle meets less resistance.

QUIZ ANSWER: Baum got it from a filing cabinet drawer, O-Z.

MAY 16th

TODAY'S THOUGHT: "You know that bank I used to cry all the way to? I bought it." —*Liberace*

HISTORY: On this date in 1929 the first Oscars were given out.

QUIZ: Who was Margaret Herrick and what unique place does she hold in the history of the Academy Awards?

Trivia

The average American spends about 3,500 hours shaving in his lifetime.

QUIZ ANSWER: She was a secretary who happened to remark that the new statuette looked like her Uncle Oscar, and the name stuck. Years later she became executive director of the academy.

MAY 17th

TODAY'S THOUGHT: "Outside of a dog, a book is a man's best friend. Inside of a dog, it's too dark to read."
—Groucho Marx

HISTORY: On this date in 1620 the first merry-go-round was introduced at a Turkish fair.

QUIZ: What was the distinction of the 1969 bestseller "Naked Came the Stranger"?

Trivia
Reindeer are superb swimmers.

QUIZ ANSWER: The book was a gag. A group of 25 writers of "Newsday" slapped it together over one weekend, each working on a separate chapter. The book was credited to Penelope Ashe, supposedly a Long Island housewife.

MAY 18th

TODAY'S THOUGHT: "I'd rather hit than have sex."
—Reggie Jackson

HISTORY: On this date in 1917 the Selective Service, better known to those eligible for the military as the "draft board", was created.

QUIZ: Who is the only player in Major League baseball history to legally run the bases backwards after hitting a home run?

Trivia
A jogger's heel strikes the ground 1,500 times a mile.

QUIZ ANSWER: Jimmy Piersall — While playing for the 1963 New York Mets, he did it to celebrate his 100th career homer. The next day the big league rulebook was changed to make this illegal.

MAY 19th

TODAY'S THOUGHT: "I have enough money to last me the rest of my life — unless I buy something."
—*Jackie Mason*

HISTORY: On this date in 1911 the long arm of the law first used fingerprints to get a conviction.

QUIZ: Are there more than a million millionaires in the United States?

Trivia
In the United States a car is stolen every thirty seconds.

QUIZ ANSWER: Yes — There are approximately 2,500,000 or one out of every hundred people.

MAY 20th

TODAY'S THOUGHT: "If it wasn't for electricity we'd all be watching television by candlelight." —*George Gobel*

HISTORY: On this date in 1927 "Lucky Lindy", Charles Augustus Lindbergh, began his successful solo flight across the Atlantic.

QUIZ: True or False? The camel drinks up to thirty gallons of water at a time, which it stores in its hump.

Trivia
A rat can go longer without water than a camel.

QUIZ ANSWER: True and false — It can drink up to thirty gallons of water but it isn't stored in the hump. Rather, it remains in pockets which line its stomach.

MAY 21st

TODAY'S THOUGHT: "According to statistics, a man eats a prune every twenty seconds. I don't know who this fellow is, but I know where to find him."
—*Morey Amsterdam*

HISTORY: On this date in 1881 Clara Barton founded the American Red Cross in Washington, D.C.

QUIZ: How many teeth does a typical dog have?

Trivia

The human tooth has approximately fifty miles of canals in it.

QUIZ ANSWER: 42 — 20 on top and 22 on the lower jaw

MAY 22nd

TODAY'S THOUGHT: "Be kind to your mother-in-law, and if necessary pay for her board at some good hotel."
—*Josh Billings*

HISTORY: On this date in 1992 it was "Therrrrrre Goes Johnny!" After a reign that spanned the Cuban Missile Crisis, Woodstock, Watergate, disco, Reagan and the Gulf War, Johnny Carson retired from "The Tonight Show".

QUIZ: Bathroom Brain Teaser: Charles Chaplin's chaplain chided Charlie constantly concerning Chaplin's cow-like chewing. How many C's are there in all?

Trivia

Last Chance Gulch, the 1860's mining camp, later changed its name to Helena and is now the capital of Montana.

QUIZ ANSWER: There are no C's in "all".

MAY 23rd

TODAY'S THOUGHT: "Mary had a little lamb. The doctor fainted." —*Anonymous*

HISTORY: On this date in 1785 Ben Franklin was old enough to need bifocals, so he invented them.

QUIZ: Can you identify the cities bearing the following nicknames?

A: Rubber capital of the world   D: Magic city
B: Pretzel city   E: The world's
C: Peanut city   playground

Trivia
Florida's state song is "Old Folks at Home".

QUIZ ANSWER: A — Akron, OH; B — Reading, PA;
C — Suffolk, VA; D — Birmingham, AL;
E — Atlantic City, NJ

MAY 24th

TODAY'S THOUGHT: "The two biggest sellers in any bookstore are the cookbooks and the diet books. The cookbooks tell you how to prepare the food, and the diet books tell you how not to eat any of it."
—*Andy Rooney*

HISTORY: On this date in 1935 baseball fans saw the light as the first major league baseball game was played at night at Crosley Field in Cincinnati.

QUIZ: Which of these is a butterfly?
A: Swallowtail   C: Fish tail
B: Fantail   D: None of the above

Trivia
IBM was originally called the Computing-Tabulating-Recording Company.

QUIZ ANSWER: A

MAY 25th

TODAY'S THOUGHT: "What can you say about a society that says that God is dead and Elvis is alive?"
—*Irv Kupcinet*

HISTORY: On this date in 1968 the Gateway Arch in St. Louis formally opened.

QUIZ: Beverly Hills, 90210 might be the country's most famous postal code but which New York City landmarks bear the zip codes 10047 and 10048?

Trivia
The Custer Battlefield Monument in Montana has the world's first solar-powered toilet.

QUIZ ANSWER: Each of the World Trade Towers in lower Manhattan has its own zip code.

MAY 26th

TODAY'S THOUGHT: "The four stages of man are infancy, childhood, adolescence and obsolescence."
—*Art Linkletter*

HISTORY: On this date in 1978 Atlantic City became the first city outside Nevada to offer legalized casino gambling.

QUIZ: True or False? In the typical American household, the television is on about four hours a day.

Trivia
Americans get almost 2 million tons of junk mail annually, using approximately 100 million trees.

QUIZ ANSWER: False — not even close. The TV is on almost 7-1/2 hours a day!

MAY 27th

TODAY'S THOUGHT: "The nice thing about being a celebrity is that when you bore people, they think it's their fault." —*Henry Kissinger*

HISTORY: On this date in 1937 the Golden Gate Bridge in San Francisco opened.

QUIZ: True or False? Henry Kissinger was named an honorary Harlem Globetrotter.

Trivia

Approximately 98% of all coupons go unused.

QUIZ ANSWER: True — Kissinger has done a lot of "globetrotting".

MAY 28th

TODAY'S THOUGHT: "Having children is like having a bowling alley installed in your brain." —*Martin Mull*

HISTORY: On this date in 1934 an international sensation began with the birth of quintuplets Cecile, Marie, Emile, Yvonne and Annette Dionne in Ontario, Canada.

QUIZ: What three animals move their front and hind legs on one side and then their front and hind legs on the other side when they walk?

Trivia

It takes a skunk three weeks to crank out one ounce of foul odor.

QUIZ ANSWER: A cat, a camel and a giraffe

MAY 29th

TODAY'S THOUGHT: "You know you are getting old when the candles cost more than the cake." —*Bob Hope*

HISTORY: On this date in 1953 Sir Edmund Hillary and Tenzing Norkay became the first men to reach the summit of Mount Everest.

QUIZ: Bathroom Brain Teaser: It's a holiday and Jeff gets into his car and drives hundreds of miles only to wind up where he started. What state and what month did Jeff drive?

Trivia

Every citizen of Kentucky is required by law to take a bath once a year.

QUIZ ANSWER: Jeff drove in May in Indiana in the Indianapolis 500.

MAY 30th

TODAY'S THOUGHT: "When a man has to make a speech, the first thing he has to decide is what to say." —*Gerald Ford*

HISTORY: On this date in 1911 the first Indy 500 was held. Ray Harroun took first place with the blistering speed of 75 miles per hour.

QUIZ: True or False? Saudi Arabia imports camels and sand.

Trivia

Birds are even more warm-blooded than mammals. A body temperature of 108 degrees in not uncommon.

QUIZ ANSWER: True — The desert sand is not suitable for building so river sand from Scotland is imported. Camels are getting scarce and must be imported from North Africa.

MAY 31st

TODAY'S THOUGHT: "I like long walks, especially when they are taken by people who annoy me."
—*Fred Allen*

HISTORY: On this date in 1965 Jim Clark cracked the 150 mph barrier to win auto racing's Indianapolis 500.

QUIZ: Who is the only swimmer to win five individual medals in a single Olympics?

Trivia

Bulls don't necessarily attack when they see a red cape; they are color-blind.

QUIZ ANSWER: Australian schoolgirl Shane Gould won three golds, a silver and a bronze in the 1972 Olympics in Munich.

JUNE 1st

TODAY'S THOUGHT: "I've been on a calendar, but never on time." —*Marilyn Monroe*

HISTORY: On this date in 1925 Lou Gehrig began his Major League career and played in the first of his 2,130 consecutive games.

QUIZ: Columbus, Ohio's Mary Campbell is the only person to win what title for two consecutive years?

Trivia

Marilyn Monroe claimed the only thing she wore to bed was Chanel Number 5.

QUIZ ANSWER: Miss America, in 1922 and 1923

JUNE 2nd

TODAY'S THOUGHT: "A diplomat is a man who always remembers a woman's birthday but never remembers her age." —*Robert Frost*

HISTORY: On this date in 1953 Elizabeth II was crowned in Westminster Abbey.

QUIZ: What is the longest running prime time network TV program?

Trivia

In the wintertime squirrels lose about half of their nuts because they forget where they stored them.

QUIZ ANSWER: On the air since 1968, it's "60 Minutes", still ticking away after all these years.

JUNE 3rd

TODAY'S THOUGHT: "Television is an invention that permits you to be entertained in your living room by people you wouldn't have in your home." —*David Frost*

HISTORY: On this date in 1888 Ernest L. Thayer's "Casey at the Bat" first appeared in the "San Francisco Examiner".

QUIZ: You have ten seconds... The name of which talk show host, spelled backwards, is one of the Marx brothers?

Trivia
Canada has more lakes than the rest of the world put together.

QUIZ ANSWER: Time's up! The answer is...Oprah.

JUNE 4th

TODAY'S THOUGHT: "A hair in the head is worth two in the brush." —*Oliver Herford*

HISTORY: On this date in 1896 Henry Ford drove the Quadricycle, his very first automobile, onto the streets of Detroit where he made it several blocks before breaking down.

QUIZ: A few decades ago, George DeMaestral took a walk in the woods. Afterwards, the cockleburs he noticed sticking to his clothing became his inspiration for what invention?

Trivia
The average person's bones weigh forty pounds.

QUIZ ANSWER: Velcro

JUNE 5th

TODAY'S THOUGHT: "Never eat anything you can't pronounce." —*Erma Bombeck*

HISTORY: On this date in 1783 man achieved sustained flight for the first time as the Montgolfier brothers of France launched their hot air balloon which rose 1,500 feet and drifted about a mile and a half before landing ten minutes later.

QUIZ: What music legend's favorite meal was a sandwich of peanut butter and bananas grilled in butter?

Trivia

The reason you haven't seen any cashews in a shell is because they don't have any. A cashew is a seed, not a nut.

QUIZ ANSWER: Elvis Presley

JUNE 6th

TODAY'S THOUGHT: "Ants can carry twenty times their own body weight, which is useful information if you're moving out and you need help getting a potato chip across town." —*Ron Darian*

HISTORY: On this date in 1944 Allied troops stormed ashore at Normandy Beach for D-Day, Operation Overload.

QUIZ: What sporting disk had its beginnings as the Pluto Platter in the fifties?

Trivia

J. Paul Getty was once a sparring partner for heavyweight champion Jack Dempsey.

QUIZ ANSWER: When inventor Fred Morrison first invented them, he called them "Morrison's Flying Saucers". Wham-O rechristened them "Pluto Platters" but changed their name once more to "Frisbee" in 1958.

JUNE 7th

TODAY'S THOUGHT: "Never hire anybody whose resume rhymes." —*Anonymous*

HISTORY: On this date in 1892 the practice of using pinch hitters in baseball began.

QUIZ: What's next in this sequence: L, C, CC, CD, ___?

Trivia

Maine is the only state surrounded on three sides by another country.

QUIZ ANSWER: DCCC — The letters are Roman numerals. L = 50; C = 100; CC = 200; CD = 400; DCCC = 800

JUNE 8th

TODAY'S THOUGHT: "When you are eight years old, nothing is any of your business." —*Lenny Bruce*

HISTORY: On this date in 1869 the housekeeper's friend, I.W. McGaffrey, received his patent for the first vacuum cleaner.

QUIZ: Which grows faster, your fingernails or toenails?

Trivia

In the Philippine jungles the yo-yo was first used as a weapon.

QUIZ ANSWER: Thumbs up for your fingernails. They grow about an inch a year, four times faster than your toenails.

JUNE 9th

TODAY'S THOUGHT: "What's another word for thesaurus?" —*Steven Wright*

HISTORY: On this date in 1869 Philadelphia drugstore owner, Charles Hires, peddled the first root beer.

QUIZ: Which part of your body is least sensitive to pain?

Trivia

Retlaw Yensid was the writer of the 1966 Disney movie, "Lt. Robin Crusoe, U.S.N." Retlaw Yensid is Walter Disney backwards.

QUIZ ANSWER: Your heel

JUNE 10th

TODAY'S THOUGHT: "I've never looked through a keyhole without finding someone was looking back." —*Judy Garland*

HISTORY: On this date in 1935 Alcoholics Anonymous was founded in New York City by "Doctor Bob" Smith and William G. Wilson.

QUIZ: In which appropriately named section of New York City was the first "Please don't squeeze the Charmin" commercial filmed?

Trivia

A chicken is the only animal that's eaten before it is born and after it is dead.

QUIZ ANSWER: In Flushing, of course — Mr. Whipple, one of the longest running commercial characters on television, was played by Dick Wilson.

JUNE 11th

TODAY'S THOUGHT: "Remember, if you save nothing, you can't take it with you." —*Stan Laurel*

HISTORY: On this date in 1770 explorer Captain Cook discovered the Great Barrier Reef off the coast of Australia - by crashing into it!

QUIZ: A pop science quiz: If H is hydrogen, I is iodine, O is oxygen and Ag is silver, how do you pronounce HIOAg?

Trivia

A snake can hear with its tongue.

QUIZ ANSWER: You don't really need any knowledge of chemistry... it's "Hi-O Silver!"

JUNE 12th

TODAY'S THOUGHT: "Grey hair is God's graffiti."
—*Bill Cosby*

HISTORY: On this date in 1939 the National Baseball Hall of Fame was dedicated in Cooperstown, New York.

QUIZ: What is the plural of graffiti?

Trivia

Football historians claim the quarterback's exclamation of "hut" for the snap stems from Army drills where the drill sergeant would count off "Hut-2-3-4".

QUIZ ANSWER: Graffiti is plural. Graffito is singular.

JUNE 13th

TODAY'S THOUGHT: "The other day I bought a wastebasket and carried it home in a paper bag. And when I got home, I put the paper bag in the wastebasket!" —*Lily Tomlin*

HISTORY: On this date in 1927 the all time greatest amount of tickertape was released above Charles Lindbergh's head as New York City showered him with affection after his history-making transatlantic solo flight.

QUIZ: Who invented the bowie knife?

Trivia

Casanova was a novel lover who ended his life as a librarian.

QUIZ ANSWER: Rezin Pleasant Bowie, Jim's brother

JUNE 14th

TODAY'S THOUGHT: "If a cluttered desk is an indication of a cluttered mind, what is indicated by an empty desk?" —*Anonymous*

HISTORY: On this date in 1951 Univac, the world's first commercial computer, was demonstrated in Philadelphia, Pennsylvania.

QUIZ: What do Cary Middlecoff, Paul Revere, Zane Grey, Casey Stengel and Edgar Buchanan have in common?

Trivia

The Alaskan flag was designed by a thirteen-year-old student who won an American Legion contest.

QUIZ ANSWER: All their careers, at one time or another, were looking down in the mouth; they were dentists.

JUNE 15th

TODAY'S THOUGHT: "You campaign in poetry. You govern in prose." —*Mario Cuomo*

HISTORY: On this date in 1752 Ben Franklin flew a kite in a thunderstorm and discovered that lightning is electricity.

QUIZ: What famous throughfare started out as Bloomingdale Road?

Trivia

The longest street in the United States is Figueroa Street in Los Angeles. It runs for thirty miles throughout the city.

QUIZ ANSWER: Had it not been changed, George M. Cohan might have written "Give My Regards to Bloomingdale Road"... It's Broadway!

JUNE 16th

TODAY'S THOUGHT: "People with honorary awards are looked upon with disfavor. Would you let an honorary mechanic fix your brand-new Mercedes?"
—*Neil Simon*

HISTORY: On this date in 1963 Valentina Tereshkova of the Soviet Union became the first female astronaut in space.

QUIZ: Name two television crime fighters whose first names were never revealed.

Trivia

The Red Sea is not red. It's a bluish-green.

QUIZ ANSWER: Lt. Columbo and Quincy, although viewers once got a peek at Quincy's first initial — R.

JUNE 17th

TODAY'S THOUGHT: "Nothing is more responsible for the good old days than a bad memory."
—*Robert Benchley*

HISTORY: On this date in 1972 the Watergate burglars broke into the offices of the Democratic National Committee.

QUIZ: Which states are nicknamed the Gopher State, the Pelican State and the Empire State of the South?

Trivia

The most common first name among U.S. presidents is James (6).

QUIZ ANSWER: Minnesota, Louisiana and Georgia, respectively

JUNE 18th

TODAY'S THOUGHT: "Why pay a dollar for a bookmark? Why not just use the dollar as a bookmark?"
—*Fred Stoller*

HISTORY: On this date in 1815 the British defeated the French in the Battle of Waterloo.

QUIZ: What two teams in Major League baseball were once known as the Washington Senators?

Trivia

The newspaper in Popeye's hometown of Sweethaven is called the "Sweethaven Daily Poop".

QUIZ ANSWER: The Minnesota Twins and the Texas Rangers — The Twins moved to Minnesota from Washington, D.C. in 1961. The newly created Washington Senators left town in 1972 and moved to Arlington, Texas.

JUNE 19th

TODAY'S THOUGHT: "They say the dog is man's best friend. I don't believe that. How many of your friends have you neutered?" —*Larry Reeb*

HISTORY: On this date in 1910, inspired by YMCA worker Mrs. John Dodd, the United States celebrated the first Father's Day, three years after Mother's Day was first celebrated.

QUIZ: What comic strip character made his first appearance on June 19, 1978?

Trivia
The energy it takes to melt a small iceberg could power a ship across the Atlantic about one hundred times.

QUIZ ANSWER: Jim Davis' "Garfield" purred his way into our hearts.

JUNE 20th

TODAY'S THOUGHT: "My problem lies in reconciling my gross habits with my net income." —*Errol Flynn*

HISTORY: On this date in 1863 the National Bank of Philadelphia was the first bank chartered by Congress.

QUIZ: Who's the only person to appear on "TV Guide's" cover three weeks in a row?

Trivia
Ida May Fuller of Vermont was the first person to receive a Social Security check. She got it in 1940 and lived to be over 100, eventually collecting more than $20,000.

QUIZ ANSWER: Michael Landon, 1991

JUNE 21st

TODAY'S THOUGHT: "The perils of duck hunting are great, especially for the duck." —*Walter Cronkite*

HISTORY: On this date in 1964 Jim Bunning pitched a perfect baseball game for the Philadelphia Phillies against the New York Mets.

QUIZ: What is Bell's Phenomenon?

Trivia

Pianist extraordinaire, Liberace, started out by giving concerts at high schools under the name of Walter Busterkeys.

QUIZ ANSWER: When eye muscles relax and the eyes roll back above their usual position, such as when we're asleep

JUNE 22nd

TODAY'S THOUGHT: "As for butter versus margarine, I trust cows more than chemists." —*Joan Gussow*

HISTORY: On this date in 1938 Joe Louis got his revenge on Max Schmeling, the only boxer who had ever beaten him. It took exactly 124 seconds for Louis to drop Schmeling.

QUIZ: Scare an elephant and...

A: it'll charge you   C: its ears will stand straight up

B: it'll rear up on   D: you'll wish you hadn't
    its hind legs

Trivia

The only dog that sweats is the Mexican hairless.

QUIZ ANSWER: C

JUNE 23rd

TODAY'S THOUGHT: "It was a lucky thing for all of us when Alexander Graham Bell made his first telephone call, the line was not busy." —*Anonymous*

HISTORY: On this date in 1980 "Late Night With David Letterman" premiered on NBC.

QUIZ: Who was the first non-American golfer to win the Masters?

Trivia

Weatherman Willard Scott was the original Ronald McDonald.

QUIZ ANSWER: South African Gary Player first won the Masters in 1961 and followed up in 1974 and 1978.

JUNE 24th

TODAY'S THOUGHT: "If law school is so hard to get through, how come there are so many lawyers?" —*Calvin Trillin*

HISTORY: On this date in 1947 the term "flying saucer" was first used to describe a UFO sighting by Kenneth Arnold of Boise, Idaho. He reported seeing nine flying saucers in formation over Mount Rainier, Washington.

QUIZ: Who was Thomas Wilson and why was he pretty well known in the early part of the twentieth century?

Trivia

The twin Popsicle was created during the Depression so that two children could share a single treat.

QUIZ ANSWER: President of the United States between 1913 and 1921, he preferred to go by his middle name, Woodrow.

The Bathroom Trivia Almanac

JUNE 25th

TODAY'S THOUGHT: "All animals are equal, but some animals are more equal than others." —*George Orwell*

HISTORY: On this date in 1876 the Battle of Little Big Horn took place. The only member of the Seventh Cavalry to survive the battle was Comanche, a horse who became a national celebrity.

QUIZ: True or False? There has never been a bachelor president in the United States.

Trivia

The most popular hobby in the world is stamp collecting.

QUIZ ANSWER: False — James Buchanan, the fifteenth president, was unhitched.

JUNE 26th

TODAY'S THOUGHT: "Big sisters are the crab grass in the lawn of life." —*Charles Schulz*

HISTORY: On this date in 1945 the United Nations charter was signed by fifty nations in San Francisco.

QUIZ: Can you name the first man-made object which traveled faster than the speed of sound?

Trivia

About the $24 Peter Minuet paid to the American Indians for Manhattan — invested at 8% compounded daily, that money would be worth more than 30 trillion dollars today.

QUIZ ANSWER: If you're thinking Concorde, you're still up in the air about this. It's the tip of a whip. The noise at the crack of the whip is caused by the tip breaking the sound barrier.

JUNE 27th

TODAY'S THOUGHT: "A man with one watch knows what time it is. A man with two is never sure."
—*John Peers*

HISTORY: On this date in 1929 Bell Labs conducted the first transmission of color television.

QUIZ: Which is the most often sung tune in the world?

Trivia
Your skin weighs twice as much as your brain.

QUIZ ANSWER: "Happy Birthday to You" — This song, composed by Kentucky schoolteacher Mildred Hill, was originally written as a song for schoolchildren and titled "Good Morning to You". Sister Patty Hill had written the words in 1893 and in 1924 the now familiar "Happy Birthday" lyrics were added.

JUNE 28th

TODAY'S THOUGHT: "Tragedy is if I cut my finger. Comedy is if I walk into an open sewer and die."
—*Mel Brooks*

HISTORY: On this date in 1914 Archduke Francis Ferdinand and his wife were assassinated at Sarajevo, Bosnia touching off the conflict that became World War I.

QUIZ: A brain-teasing thought for the throne: How can you make six sixes (666666) equal 67?

Trivia
In Tiddlywinks, the art of flipping the winks into a cup is called "potting".

QUIZ ANSWER: 66+66/66

JUNE 29th

TODAY'S THOUGHT: "Blessed are the young, for they shall inherit the national debt." —*Herbert Hoover*

HISTORY: On this date in 1949 the United States withdrew its troops from Korea.

QUIZ: Dolphins sleep with one eye open all the time— and that's no fish story, but do you know the only members of the animal kingdom to commonly sleep on their backs?

Trivia

Red schoolhouses were painted red because it was the cheapest color paint.

QUIZ ANSWER: Those animals are human beings.

JUNE 30th

TODAY'S THOUGHT: "Did you ever notice that when you blow into a dog's face he gets mad, but when you take him in a car he sticks his head out the window?" —*Steve Bluestein*

HISTORY: On this date in 1971 the 26th Amendment was ratified giving the vote to eighteen-year-olds.

QUIZ: What do these sentences have in common?
  Pack my box with five dozen liquor jugs.
  The five boxing wizards jump quickly.
  The quick brown fox jumps over a lazy dog.

Trivia

"Chop suey" means "odds and ends".

QUIZ ANSWER: They are pangrams — a sentence that includes every letter of the alphabet.

JULY 1st

TODAY'S THOUGHT: "The wonderful world of appliances now makes it possible to cook indoors with charcoal and outdoors with gas." —*Bill Vaughan*

HISTORY: On this date in 1862 the Bureau of Internal Revenue was established by an act of Congress.

QUIZ: In which city did the first United States zoo open?

Trivia

The 1,500 pound leatherback turtle carries a shell that is as big as a king size bed, but a lot harder to find fitted sheets for.

QUIZ ANSWER: On July 1, 1874 the first zoo opened in Philadelphia with 1,000 animals on display. There were 3,000 visitors with admission costing adults 25 cents and children 10 cents.

JULY 2nd

TODAY'S THOUGHT: "America is the only country in the world where you can burn the flag but can't tear the tag off the mattress." —*Jackie Mason*

HISTORY: On this date in 1937 aviatrix Amelia Earhart disappeared over the Pacific.

QUIZ: What French word, spelled backwards, gives its English translation — a word which describes how the U.S. is made up?

Trivia

The average magazine lies around the house for 29 weeks before someone gets around to throwing it out.

QUIZ ANSWER: États

JULY 3rd

TODAY'S THOUGHT: "Age is a high price to pay for maturity." —*Tom Stoppard*

HISTORY: On this date in 1976 an Israeli commando unit raided the Entebbe airport in Uganda and rescued 103 hostages from a hijacked Air France plane.

QUIZ: Bathroom Brain Teaser: Which of the following letter designs does not belong with the other six?

Y   E   N   F   H   A   Z

Trivia

An avocado has 370 calories, the greatest number of any fruit.

QUIZ ANSWER: The letter E, which is made of four straight lines

JULY 4th

TODAY'S THOUGHT: "Television has proved that people will look at anything rather than each other."
—*Ann Landers*

HISTORY: On this date in 1826 both Thomas Jefferson and John Adams died. In 1831 a third president, James Monroe, also died on July 4.

QUIZ: Which continually published reference work in the English language has been around the longest?

Trivia

Calvin Coolidge was the only president to have been sworn in by his own father.

QUIZ ANSWER: The "Encyclopaedia Brittannica" has been in existence since the mid 1700's. Incidentally, George Washington owned a set of the third edition.

JULY 5th

TODAY'S THOUGHT: "Every crowd has a silver lining."
—*P.T. Barnum*

HISTORY: On this date in 1841 the first travel agency, Thomas Cook & Sons, was founded in London.

QUIZ: Can you name the only major sport where you play defense when you have the ball?

Trivia

When Oreo cookies were first made, they were mound-shaped. The name comes from the Greek word "oreo" which means "hill".

QUIZ ANSWER: Baseball

JULY 6th

TODAY'S THOUGHT: "No matter how thin you slice it, it's still baloney." —*Alfred E. Smith*

HISTORY: On this date in 1933 the first All-Star game was played with the American League winning 4-2.

QUIZ: What city is located on two continents?

Trivia

"Double hemisphere action" is the term used for the ability to write, simultaneously, something completely different with both your left and right hands.

QUIZ ANSWER: Istanbul, Turkey is in both Asia and Europe.

JULY 7th

TODAY'S THOUGHT: "I was stopped once for going 53 in a 35 mph zone, but I told them I had dyslexia."
—*Spanky McFarland*

HISTORY: On this date in 1891 the patent was issued for traveler's checks.

QUIZ: Let's play "Jeopardy!" He was the show's first host, appearing on 1,858 shows between 1964 and 1979. And the question is...?

Trivia

The Lone Ranger's sidekick was played by Jay Silverheels who was born Harold J. Smith.

QUIZ ANSWER: Who is Art Fleming?

JULY 8th

TODAY'S THOUGHT: "There are three periods in life: youth, middle age and 'how well you look'."
—*Nelson Rockefeller*

HISTORY: On this date in 1835 the Liberty Bell cracked — again — while tolling the death of the first Chief Justice, John Marshall.

QUIZ: Which state has the most miles of highway and the most vehicles per square mile?

Trivia

The first person to be arrested for speeding was a New York City cab driver. On May 20, 1899 Jacob German was arrested for doing a breakneck 12 mph.

QUIZ ANSWER: The Garden State, New Jersey

JULY 9th

TODAY'S THOUGHT: "Fear of losing is what makes competitors so great. Show me a gracious loser and I'll show you a perennial loser." —*O.J. Simpson*

HISTORY: On this date in 1872 the patent was issued for the doughnut cutter.

QUIZ: Sixties Flashback: What pitcher had the dubious distinction of serving up Roger Maris' record breaking 61st home run?

Trivia

The K in K-Mart stands for Kresge, from Sebastian S. Kresge who founded the store in Detroit in 1897.

QUIZ ANSWER: Tracy Stallard of the Red Sox

JULY 10th

TODAY'S THOUGHT: "I think God invented rain to give dead people something to complain about." —*David Brenner*

HISTORY: On this date in 1958 the world's heaviest man, Robert Earl Hughes of Monticello, Illinois passed away. Weighing approximately a half ton, he was buried in a piano case.

QUIZ: Which Ohio town doesn't belong and why? (Hint: "A man a plan a canal, Panama!")
A: Ada   B: Akron   C: Anna   D: Ava

Trivia

The average American laughs fifteen times a day.

QUIZ ANSWER: B — The other towns are all palindromes (words that read the same backward and forward). Wow!

JULY 11th

TODAY'S THOUGHT: "When I am dead and buried, on my tombstone I would like to have it written, 'I have arrived.' Because when you feel that you have arrived, you are dead." —*Yul Brynner*

HISTORY: On this date in 1804 Alexander Hamilton and Vice-President Aaron Burr held their duel. Hamilton missed... Burr didn't.

QUIZ: Which is taller, St. Louis' Gateway Arch or the Washington Monument in Washington, D.C.?

Trivia
Your nose and ears never stop growing.

QUIZ ANSWER: The Gateway Arch, at 630 feet, is 75 feet taller than the Washington Monument.

JULY 12th

TODAY'S THOUGHT: "I never found the companion that was so companionable as solitude."
—*Henry David Thoreau*

HISTORY: On this date in 1862 the Congressional Medal of Honor was created.

QUIZ: In an average lifetime, an American drinks about:
A: 2,000 gallons of water   D: 11,000 gallons of water
B: 4,000 gallons of water   E: 120,000 gallons of water
C: 6,000 gallons of water

Trivia
Each of your toes has three bones except for your big toe which has but two.

QUIZ ANSWER: D — 11,000 gallons of water

JULY 13th

TODAY'S THOUGHT: "Too often we... enjoy the comfort of opinion without the discomfort of thought."
—*John F. Kennedy*

HISTORY: On this date in 1960 the Democratic Party nominated John F. Kennedy for president.

QUIZ: You've spent countless hours watching "The Honeymooners", but do you know what famous comedian did a guest stint as the Kramden's landlord?

Trivia

Dogs are more likely to have a nervous breakdown than any other non-human animal.

QUIZ ANSWER: Ralph had good reason to call the landlord stingy... he was played in one episode by Jack Benny.

JULY 14th

TODAY'S THOUGHT: "Celibacy is not hereditary."
—*Guy Goden*

HISTORY: On this date in 1881 Sheriff Pat Garrett shot and killed Billy the Kid.

QUIZ: Did America ever have a King for president?

Trivia

The only president to attend the Indy 500 was Gerald Ford in 1979.

QUIZ ANSWER: Yes, former President Gerald R. Ford was born Leslie King. He has the distinction of being the only nonelected vice-president and president in United States history.

JULY 15th

TODAY'S THOUGHT: "Rise early. Work late. Strike oil."
—*J. Paul Getty*

HISTORY: On this date in 1933 Wiley Post took off from New York in a Lockheed Vega, thus beginning the first around-the-world flight.

QUIZ: Name the three states in the U.S. that begin and end with the letter "A".

Trivia
The oldest bridegroom in history was Ralph Cambridge who was 105 when he tied the knot with his 70-year-old bride, Adriana Kapp.

QUIZ ANSWER: Alabama, Alaska and Arizona

JULY 16th

TODAY'S THOUGHT: "If President Lincoln were alive today, he'd roll over in his grave." —*Gerald R. Ford*

HISTORY: On this date in 1790 legislation was signed by George Washington selecting the District of Columbia as the permanent capital of the United States.

QUIZ: The winner of what race wins the Borg-Warner trophy?

Trivia
Composer Johann Sebastian Bach had 20 children.

QUIZ ANSWER: The Indianapolis 500

JULY 17th

TODAY'S THOUGHT: "Never go to bed mad. Stay up and fight." —*Phyllis Diller*

HISTORY: On this date in 1941 Joe DiMaggio's record 56 game hitting streak came to an end when he went 0-3 against the Cleveland Indians.

QUIZ: I sold my rights to the lyrics of "The Battle Hymn of the Republic" to a magazine for four dollars. Who am I?

Trivia

Dorothy's pet cow in "The Wizard of Oz" was named Imogene.

QUIZ ANSWER: Julia Ward Howe

JULY 18th

TODAY'S THOUGHT: "I'm desperately trying to figure out why kamikaze pilots wore helmets." —*Dave Edison*

HISTORY: On this date in 1969 Edward Kennedy's car plunged off the Chappaquiddick Bridge killing passenger Mary Jo Kopechne.

QUIZ: Bathroom Brain Teaser: June 21, the first day of summer, is called the longest day of the year. What day is actually longer?

Trivia

U.S. presidents U.S. Grant, William Howard Taft, Herbert Hoover and Dwight D. Eisenhower never held any other elective office.

QUIZ ANSWER: The day the clocks are turned back to end Daylight Savings Time, which is 25 hours

JULY 19th

TODAY'S THOUGHT: "Never run after your hat — others will be delighted to do it; why spoil their fun?"
—*Mark Twain*

HISTORY: On this date in 1990 baseball great Pete Rose was sentenced to 5 months in prison, 3 months in a halfway house, plus 1,000 hours community service and a $50,000 fine for cheating on his taxes.

QUIZ: Can you name the TV character who was so popular that when she died of a stroke in 1980, "Newsweek" ran a half-page obituary?

Trivia
Every single hamster in the U.S. today comes from a single litter captured in Syria in 1930.

QUIZ ANSWER: Edith Bunker of TV's "All in the Family"

JULY 20th

TODAY'S THOUGHT: "The greater the fool the better the dancer." —*Theodore Hook*

HISTORY: On this date in 1969 the lunar module from Apollo XI landed on the moon.

QUIZ: Two letters of the alphabet are not used on either a push-button or rotary telephone. Do you know both of them?

Trivia
The oldest subway in the world went into service in 1863 in London.

QUIZ ANSWER: Q and Z

JULY 21st

TODAY'S THOUGHT: "Have you ever wondered if illiterate people get the full effect of alphabet soup?"
—*John Mendoza*

HISTORY: On this date in 1925 the Monkey Trial ended with John Scopes being fined $100 for teaching the theory of evolution.

QUIZ: Besides deep water, what additional deterrent did medieval moats offer against those invaders who wanted to storm the castle?

Trivia

Horatio Alger is a most prolific author with publication of 119 full length novels in 30 years.

QUIZ ANSWER: The moat also served as a sewer.

JULY 22nd

TODAY'S THOUGHT: "If you're hanging around with nothing to do and the zoo is closed, come over to the Senate. You'll get the same kind of feeling and you won't have to pay." —*Robert Dole*

HISTORY: On this date in 1934 John Dillinger, Public Enemy #1, was gunned down by federal agents in Chicago after being betrayed by the woman in red.

QUIZ: Which one of these famous generals graduated number one in his class at West Point?
A: Douglas MacArthur   C: William Westmoreland
B: Dwight Eisenhower   D: George Patton

Trivia

The largest fruit crop on earth is grapes.

QUIZ ANSWER: A — All of the others failed to finish within the top 45 of their graduating class.

JULY 23rd

TODAY'S THOUGHT: "If you want to know how old a woman is, ask her sister-in-law." —*Ed Howe*

HISTORY: On this date in 1984 Vanessa Williams became the first Miss America to resign after photographs of her surfaced and scandalized the executives of the pageant.

QUIZ: What baseball feat was Sal Durante famous for in 1961?

Trivia

In 1960 Michael Eufemia had the world's longest continuous run in a straight pool match, sinking 625 balls without a miss.

QUIZ ANSWER: He is the baseball fan who caught Roger Maris' record breaking 61st home run.

JULY 24th

TODAY'S THOUGHT: "The problem with cats is that they get the exact same look for a moth or an ax murderer."
—*Paula Poundstone*

HISTORY: On this date in 1701 Antoine de la Mothe Cadillac, in the service of Louis XIV of France, landed at the site of Detroit. And, yes, the Cadillac car was named for him.

QUIZ: What group has also been dubbed "The Invisible Empire of the South"?

Trivia
A watermelon is 92 percent water.

QUIZ ANSWER: The Ku Klux Klan

JULY 25th

TODAY'S THOUGHT: "Any kid will run any errand for you, if you ask at bedtime." —*Red Skelton*

HISTORY: On this date in 1866 Ulysses S. Grant was named General of the Army, the first officer in the United States to hold that rank.

QUIZ: What do the names Chang, Schultz and Smith have in common?

Trivia

Do you sleep in your birthday suit? 20% of men and 6% of women say they do.

QUIZ ANSWER: They are the most common last names in China, Germany and the U.S. respectively. Chang is the most popular name in the world.

JULY 26th

TODAY'S THOUGHT: "She had lost the art of conversation, but not, unfortunately, the power of speech." —*George Bernard Shaw*

HISTORY: On this date in 1947 the Department of Defense, the National Security Council and the CIA were founded.

QUIZ: You've heard of the term "south of the Mason-Dixon line", but exactly where is the Mason-Dixon line?

Trivia

Although Illinois license plates boast "Land of Lincoln", until he was an adult Abe Lincoln had never set foot in Illinois.

QUIZ ANSWER: It is a 244 mile long dividing line that marks the southern boundary of Pennsylvania. In actuality, such places as part of New Jersey and Washington D.C. are south of the line.

JULY 27th

TODAY'S THOUGHT: "Baseball is ninety percent mental, and the other half is physical." —*Yogi Berra*

HISTORY: On this date in 1940 "Billboard" magazine published its first top selling record chart.

QUIZ: What are the only three words in the English language that begin with "dw"? How about the only four letter word which ends in "eny"?

Trivia

Statistics show that Saturday is the most dangerous day to drive an automobile.

QUIZ ANSWER: Dwarf, dwell and dwindle form the trio. Deny cannot be denied as the answer to the second part of the quiz.

JULY 28th

TODAY'S THOUGHT: "The one thing I do not want to be called is First Lady. It sounds like a saddle horse." —*Jacqueline Kennedy*

HISTORY: On this date in 1933 the very first singing telegram was delivered, wishing a happy birthday to Rudy Vallee.

QUIZ: What happens to your social security number when you die?

Trivia

When you breathe, the speed of your exhaled air is about 15 miles per hour.

QUIZ ANSWER: The numbers are retired, naturally. The nine digit combination gives them about one billion to choose from, so unless we extend benefits to the rest of the world, we have plenty of numbers left.

JULY 29th

TODAY'S THOUGHT: "They say you can't do it, but sometimes it doesn't always work." —*Casey Stengel*

HISTORY: On this date in 1958 NASA was founded.

QUIZ: Bathroom Brain Teaser: Muggsy is on trial in front of a jury of his peers. He's found not guilty, yet the judge sends him to prison with no possible parole. How come?

Trivia

The Empire State Building has 10 million bricks and 6,400 windows.

QUIZ ANSWER: He was already serving a life sentence for a different crime.

JULY 30th

TODAY'S THOUGHT: "How you lose or keep your hair depends on how wisely you choose your parents."
—*Edward R. Nida*

HISTORY: On this date in 1975 James R. Hoffa was last seen outside a restaurant in Michigan. Seven years and 131 days later, on December 8, 1982 Hoffa was declared legally dead.

QUIZ: What is the only food that doesn't spoil?

Trivia

It was (and maybe still is) illegal to wear roller skates in a Portland, Oregon restroom.

QUIZ ANSWER: Honey

JULY 31st

TODAY'S THOUGHT: "Artificial hearts are nothing new. Politicians have had them for years."
—*Mac McGinnis*

HISTORY: On this date in 1981 MTV made its debut.

QUIZ: Which heart beats faster, an elephant's or a canary's?

Trivia

James Whistler had to buy back his most famous painting, "Whistler's Mother", from a pawnshop after his mother passed away.

QUIZ ANSWER: The canary's beats at a much heartier rate — 1,000 times a minute compared to the 27 times per minute of an elephant's heart.

AUGUST 1st

TODAY'S THOUGHT: "An utterly fearless man is a far more dangerous comrade than a coward."
—*Herman Melville*

HISTORY: On this date in 1790 the first United States census resulted in a head count of about four million people...more than that now work for the government!

QUIZ: What fateful contact did the Lincoln family have with the Booth family prior to 1865?

Trivia
A pig always sleeps on its right side.

QUIZ ANSWER: In one of the strangest coincidences in history, one day in Jersey City a young Robert Todd Lincoln, Abe's son, fell between railroad cars and was rescued by actor Edwin Booth, brother of John Wilkes Booth.

AUGUST 2nd

TODAY'S THOUGHT: "Children have never been very good at listening to their elders, but they have never failed to imitate them." —*James Baldwin*

HISTORY: On this date in 1873 the San Francisco cable car had its first trial run.

QUIZ: What nation used to be the kingdom of Siam?

Trivia
Only three percent of Norway is under cultivation — the rest is under ice.

QUIZ ANSWER: Thailand used to be Siam, if you please.

AUGUST 3rd

TODAY'S THOUGHT: "If you go long enough without a bath, even the fleas will let you alone." —*Ernie Pyle*

HISTORY: On this date in 1492 Christopher Columbus set sail from Spain on his way to the New World and the discovery of America. The voyage cost about $7,000 which included his personal salary of $300 a year.

QUIZ: Bathroom Brain Teaser: A boy borrowed a book from the library with the words "How to Hum" printed on it. When he opened it at home, he discovered it was not about humming at all. What was it?

Trivia
Over one million drawings went into the movie production of "Pinocchio".

QUIZ ANSWER: Part of an encyclopedia

AUGUST 4th

TODAY'S THOUGHT: "If there were any justice in the world, people would be able to fly over pigeons for a change." —*Anonymous*

HISTORY: On this date in 1693 Dom Perignon invented champagne. Now, if you could find a bottle of that vintage, you'd really have something!

QUIZ: Where are 85 percent of all the plants in the world located?

Trivia
Manhole covers are made round because they can't fall through the manhole itself. Other shapes can.

QUIZ ANSWER: Most plants live in the oceans.

AUGUST 5th

TODAY'S THOUGHT: "Early to bed, early to rise, and your girl goes out with other guys." —*Bob Collins*

HISTORY: On this date in 1957 Dick Clark began hosting "American Bandstand" on ABC.

QUIZ: Match the portrait with the U.S. paper currency:

1 — Thomas Jefferson   A: $1,000
2 — James Madison   B: $ 500
3 — Grover Cleveland   C: $5,000
4 — William McKinley   D: $ 2

Trivia

If you take a penny and double it, and then keep doubling it every day for thirty days, you will wind up with over five million dollars.

QUIZ ANSWER: 1 — D; 2 — C; 3 — A; 4 — B

AUGUST 6th

TODAY'S THOUGHT: "If God wanted us to be brave, why did he give us legs?" —*Marvin Kitman*

HISTORY: On this date in 1926 Gertrude Ederle became the first woman to swim the English Channel.

QUIZ: What incredible automobile record was set in 1930 by Charles Creighton and James Hargis?

Trivia

Roller skates, which originally consisted of four wheels on rubber pads, were invented about 1860.

QUIZ ANSWER: They drove cross country without stopping the engine of their Model A roadster. After arriving in Los Angeles they immediately drove back to New York, completing the 7,180 mile round trip in 42 days — completely in reverse.

AUGUST 7th

TODAY'S THOUGHT: "It was luxuries like air conditioning that brought down the Roman Empire. With air conditioning their windows were shut; they couldn't hear the barbarians coming." —*Garrison Keillor*

HISTORY: On this date in 1888 Theophilus Van Kannel of Philadelphia received the patent for the revolving door.

QUIZ: Can you name the only New England state without a seacoast?

Trivia

A violin contains seventy separate pieces of wood.

QUIZ ANSWER: Vermont

AUGUST 8th

TODAY'S THOUGHT: "Of all my wife's relations I like myself the best." —*Joe Cook*

HISTORY: On this date in 1963 "The Great Train Robbery" netted $7 million for a gang of British crooks.

QUIZ: Where did Henry Heinz get the number "57" for his famous slogan "57 Varieties"?

Trivia

Smithsonian Institution founder James Smith never set foot in the United States.

QUIZ ANSWER: Even back in 1892 when the pickle potentate cooked up the slogan, the company was making far more products than that. He was simply fascinated by the number 57 and felt it was lucky for him. It was, and for dozens of heirs as well. You might say the whole family relishes the number.

AUGUST 9th

TODAY'S THOUGHT: "Anyone who says he can see through women is missing a lot." —*Groucho Marx*

HISTORY: On this date in 1974 Richard Nixon took his final bow as he resigned the presidency.

QUIZ: When he started the American Messenger Company in 1907 in Seattle, Jim Casey was 19 years old. By the end of World War I, his tiny messenger service had grown considerably and he changed its name to what current outfit?

Trivia

The Union Army lost more men to disease than battle during the Civil War.

QUIZ ANSWER: United Parcel Service

AUGUST 10th

TODAY'S THOUGHT: "I don't think anybody should write his autobiography until after he's dead."
—*Samuel Goldwyn*

HISTORY: On this date in 1981 Pete Rose to the occasion and broke Stan Musial's National League record of 3,630 hits. Rose would later become baseball's all-time hit leader.

QUIZ: Two days a year there are no major professional team sporting events. What are they?

Trivia

Herbert Hoover was the first president to have a phone on his desk.

QUIZ ANSWER: The day before and the day after Major League baseball's All-Star game

AUGUST 11th

TODAY'S THOUGHT: "I would have made a good Pope."
—*Richard Nixon*

HISTORY:

On this date in 1934 the first prisoners arrived on "The Rock", Alcatraz, San Francisco Bay.

QUIZ: Name "Time" magazine's Man of the Year in:

A: 1938   B: 1930   C: 1927

Trivia

Mary Phelps Jacobs patented the first brassiere in November of 1914.

QUIZ ANSWER: A — Adolph Hitler; B — Mahatma Gandhi; C — Charles Lindbergh

AUGUST 12th

TODAY'S THOUGHT: "The human race is faced with a cruel choice: work or daytime television." —*Anonymous*

HISTORY: On this date in 1977 the prototype space shuttle, Enterprise, made its maiden flight within the earth's atmosphere, launched from a 747.

QUIZ: Bathroom Brain Teaser: Is there better than a 50-50 chance that the next U.S. Tennis Open champion will have more than the average number of arms?

Trivia

Thomas Edison was hard of hearing and often communicated with his wife in Morse Code.

QUIZ ANSWER: Yes. Since the average number of arms on a human is slightly less than two, anyone with two arms has more than the average.

AUGUST 13th

TODAY'S THOUGHT: "Give them pleasure — the same pleasure they have when they wake up from a nightmare." —*Alfred Hitchcock*

HISTORY: On this date in 1961 the East German government closed the border between East and West Berlin. The Berlin Wall was built later that week and stood until 1989.

QUIZ: What was Alfred Hitchcock's given name?

Trivia
In Japan the most common name to see in the phone book in Minoru Suzukis.

QUIZ ANSWER: Joseph

AUGUST 14th

TODAY'S THOUGHT: "If the income tax is the price we have to pay to keep the government on its feet, alimony is the price we have to pay for sweeping a woman off hers." —*Groucho Marx*

HISTORY: On this date in 1945 VJ Day ended World War II. Millions took to the street in celebration and the postwar era began.

QUIZ: True or False? During World War II the National Football League's Philadelphia Eagles and Pittsburgh Steelers merged to form the Steagles.

Trivia
If you're the typical American man, you own 22 ties.

QUIZ ANSWER: True (because of the shortage of players due to the war effort)

AUGUST 15th

TODAY'S THOUGHT: "The difference between divorce and legal separation is that a legal separation gives a husband time to hide his money." —*Johnny Carson*

HISTORY: On this date in 1935 Will Rogers and Wiley Post perished in an Alaskan plane crash.

QUIZ: What high-water mark of the flower power generation took place in 1969 on this date?

Trivia

Queen Elizabeth I suffered from smallpox and was completely bald by the age of 29.

QUIZ ANSWER: The Woodstock Music and Art Fair began on this date in Bethel, New York drawing over 400,000 people and featuring 24 bands over three days.

AUGUST 16th

TODAY'S THOUGHT: "Pro football is like nuclear warfare. There are no winners, only survivors."
—*Frank Gifford*

HISTORY: On this date in 1977 came the news from Memphis that the King was dead, but it seems that it didn't take. Ever since he has been spotted at filling stations, 7-11's and Mr. Donut Shops all over the heartland.

QUIZ: What is the most watched movie film in history?

Trivia

Arlington National Cemetery was once the site of Robert E. Lee's home.

QUIZ ANSWER: "The Wizard of Oz" (seen by more than a billion people)

AUGUST 17th

TODAY'S THOUGHT: "When women kiss, it always reminds me of prizefighters shaking hands."
—*H.L. Mencken*

HISTORY: On this date in 1807 Robert Fulton's steamboat, the Clermont, sailed up the Hudson River from New York City to Albany.

QUIZ: Do you know the only word in the English language which ends in sede?

Trivia
A man's beard grows about an inch in eight weeks.

QUIZ ANSWER: Supersede

AUGUST 18th

TODAY'S THOUGHT: "No one has ever bet enough on a winning horse." —*Richard Sasuly*

HISTORY: On this date in 1859 French stuntman, the Great Blondin, crossed Niagara Falls on a tightrope while carrying a man on his shoulders.

QUIZ: What famous first did Virginia Dare accomplish on this date in 1587?

Trivia
Blood takes about 23 seconds to make one round trip of your body.

QUIZ ANSWER: Virginia was born, becoming the first child of English parents born in the New World at Roanoke Island, North Carolina.

AUGUST 19th

TODAY'S THOUGHT: "To keep your marriage brimming,
With love in the loving cup,
Whenever you're wrong, admit it;
Whenever you're right, shut up." —*Ogden Nash*

HISTORY: On this date in 1888 the first beauty contest was held at Spa, Belgium.

QUIZ: What term, in almost every language, begins with an "m" sound?

Trivia

There are 140 languages spoken around the world and each is spoken by more than one million people.

QUIZ ANSWER: Mother

AUGUST 20th

TODAY'S THOUGHT: "A good rule of thumb is if you've made it to thirty-five and your job still requires you to wear a name tag, you've probably made a serious vocational error." —*Dennis Miller*

HISTORY: On this date in 1882 Tchaikovsky's "1812 Overture" premiered in Moscow.

QUIZ: Seventies Flashback: What was television's top rated show in 1970?

Trivia

About one in six people is an habitual fingernail biter.

QUIZ ANSWER: Robert Young was the Prince of Primetime as "Marcus Welby, M.D."

AUGUST 21st

TODAY'S THOUGHT: "Happiness is having a large, loving, caring, close-knit family in another city." —*George Burns*

HISTORY: On this date in 1959 the flag got its full complement of stars as Hawaii became the last state to join the union.

QUIZ: If only the female mosquito bites, what does the male mosquito live on?

Trivia
A mosquito's favorite aroma is aftershave.

QUIZ ANSWER: While the female mosquito's reproductive needs call for blood, the male is a non-aggressive vegetarian who lives on plant nectar.

AUGUST 22nd

TODAY'S THOUGHT: "There are no liberals behind steering wheels." —*Russell Baker*

HISTORY: On this date in 1851 the yacht *America* defeated fourteen British vessels to win the first America's Cup.

QUIZ: Name a popular professional sport that requires all metal shoes.

Trivia
If you plan on being buried in a standard grave your permanent "living" quarters will be 7'8" long X 3'2" wide and, of course, 6' deep.

QUIZ ANSWER: Horse racing

AUGUST 23rd

TODAY'S THOUGHT: "We have met the enemy, and he is us." —*Walt Kelly*

HISTORY: On this date in 1989 Victoria Brucker of San Pedro, California became the first U.S. girl to play in the Little League World Series.

QUIZ: True or False? Chicago is nicknamed the "Windy City" because of its blustery politicians.

Trivia
Woodpeckers don't get headaches.

QUIZ ANSWER: True — Its long-winded politicians were the reason for the nickname. In fact, weatherwise Chicago ranks sixteenth, with an average wind speed of 10.4 miles per hour.

AUGUST 24th

TODAY'S THOUGHT: "Cordless phones are great. If you can find them." —*Glenn Foster*

HISTORY: On this date in 79 A.D. Mount Vesuvius erupted in southern Italy. The falling lava and ash entombed the cities of Pompeii, Herculaneum and Stabiae.

QUIZ: If you saw Virginia Katherine McMath and Frederick Austerlitz in a movie, what would they most likely be doing?

Trivia
Of the 3,000 islands that comprise the Bahamas chain in the Caribbean, only 20 are inhabited.

QUIZ ANSWER: Dancing — They are Ginger Rogers and Fred Astaire.

AUGUST 25th

TODAY'S THOUGHT: "What is it about American fathers as they grow older that makes them dress like flags from other countries?" —*Cary Odes*

HISTORY: On this date in 1940 the first couple ever to take the plunge with a parachute wedding tied the knot while pulling the ripcord.

QUIZ: How long do baby kangaroos stay in their mother's pouch after birth?

Trivia

A gnu has the feet of an antelope, the mane and body of an ass, the head and humped shoulders of a buffalo and the beard of a goat.

QUIZ ANSWER: It is about eight months more until they hop to it and finally give up womb and board.

AUGUST 26th

TODAY'S THOUGHT: "I have a microwave fireplace. You can lay down in front of the fire all night in eight minutes." —*Stephen Wright*

HISTORY: On this date in 1920 the 29th Amendment was enacted, giving women the right to vote.

QUIZ: As you look at it, which way does the eagle's head face on the flip side of a quarter?

Trivia

Sir Winston Churchill was the first honorary citizen of the United States.

QUIZ ANSWER: Left

AUGUST 27th

TODAY'S THOUGHT: "A vegetarian is a person who won't eat anything that can have children."
—*David Brenner*

HISTORY: On this date in 1965 the Fab Four met the King as the Beatles had an audience with Elvis in his Los Angeles digs.

QUIZ: What is the longest running show on television?

Trivia

Lyndon Johnson's favorite drink was Fresca. He had special taps installed in the White House to dispense the drink.

QUIZ ANSWER: "Meet the Press" which debuted on November 20, 1947

AUGUST 28th

TODAY'S THOUGHT: "Friends may come and go but enemies accumulate." —*Thomas Jones*

HISTORY: On this date in 1963 Dr. Martin Luther King, Jr. made his "I have a dream..." speech in Washington, D.C.

QUIZ: Who "discovered" the Gulf Stream?

Trivia

A hurricane, typhoon and cyclone are all the same thing.

QUIZ ANSWER: Benjamin Franklin proposed and mapped the Gulf Stream as his answer to a longstanding problem of commerce and navigation: why did it take some ships two weeks longer to cross the Atlantic than others with slightly different courses? Serious investigation of the phenomenon began about a century after Franklin figured it out.

AUGUST 29th

TODAY'S THOUGHT: "Fishing is a delusion entirely surrounded by liars in old clothes." —*Don Marquis*

HISTORY: On this date in 1885 Gottlieb Daimler became the first "biker" when he got a patent on the world's original motorcycle.

QUIZ: On the long running TV whodunit, "Murder, She Wrote", what is the middle name of Angela Lansbury's character?

Trivia
Cottage cheese is so-called because, in Europe as far back as the Middle Ages, farmers made the cheese in their own cottages from leftover milk after the cream had been skimmed from it for buttermaking.

QUIZ ANSWER: Her name is Jessica Beatrice Fletcher.

AUGUST 30th

TODAY'S THOUGHT: "If you don't think too good, don't think too much." —*Ted Williams*

HISTORY: On this date in 1991 Mike Powell leaped 29 feet, 4-1/2 inches to break the previous long-jump record of 29 feet, 2-1/2 inches held by Bob Beamon.

QUIZ: How is "par" on a golf hole determined?

Trivia
Lee Trevino, Jerry Heard and Bobby Nichols were all struck by lightning during the same golf tournament in 1975.

QUIZ ANSWER: Par, meaning equal, is ideally the point at which the course and a top notch golfer are evenly matched, but it is determined by the length of the hole and the sex of the golfer. For instance, a man's par 3 hole is anything up to 250 yards. A woman's par 3 is only up to 210 yards.

AUGUST 31st

TODAY'S THOUGHT: "Few things are harder to put up with than a good example." —*Mark Twain*

HISTORY: On this date in 1963 Walter Cronkite began his 18 year stint as anchorman on the "CBS Evening News".

QUIZ: By what name is William Jefferson Blythe IV better known?

Trivia

The 1944 World Series was played by two teams from the same city and in the same park. The St. Louis Browns played the St. Louis Cardinals at Sportsman's Park.

QUIZ ANSWER: Bill Clinton — The U.S. president was named after his late father and at age 16 he legally changed his name to that of his stepfather.

SEPTEMBER 1st

TODAY'S THOUGHT: "We're all in this together — by ourselves." —*Lily Tomlin*

HISTORY: On this date in 1972 the great chess war ended as Bobby Fischer defeated Boris Spassky for the world title.

QUIZ: Bathroom Brain Teaser: The 22nd and 24th presidents of the U.S. had the same mother and the same father, yet they were not brothers. Why not?

Trivia
The first modern traffic light stopped traffic on Euclid Avenue in Cleveland in 1914.

QUIZ ANSWER: They were the same man, Grover Cleveland, who served as president from 1885 to 1889 and from 1893 to 1897.

SEPTEMBER 2nd

TODAY'S THOUGHT: "The meek shall inherit the earth. They won't have the nerve to refuse it."
—*Jackie Vernon*

HISTORY: On this date in 1944 Navy pilot George Bush was shot down by the Japanese during a World War II bombing run in the Bonin Islands. Bush was rescued but his two crew members died.

QUIZ: True or False? Jim Thorpe's Indian name was "Swift-Running Deer".

Trivia
In the U.S. a baby is born every 8-1/2 seconds.

QUIZ ANSWER: False — Thorpe's Indian name was "Bright Path".

SEPTEMBER 3rd

TODAY'S THOUGHT: "One of the advantages bowling has over golf is that you seldom lose a bowling ball." —*Don Carter*

HISTORY: On this date in 1930 the first electric train, one of Thomas Edison's last inventions, began service between Hoboken and Montclair in New Jersey.

QUIZ: In a baseball game box score, what word's last letter was selected to indicate a strikeout?

Trivia
Irving Berlin was the only person in the history of the Academy of Motion Picture Arts and Sciences ever to present the Oscar to himself.

QUIZ ANSWER: Struck

SEPTEMBER 4th

TODAY'S THOUGHT: "The history of things that didn't happen has never been written." —*Henry Kissinger*

HISTORY: On this date in 1972 swimmer Mark Spitz won a record 7th gold medal in the 400-meter relay at the Olympic Games in Munich, Germany.

QUIZ: You may have some "degree" of difficulty with this one. What word in the English language has no vowels (and no y, either)?

Trivia
The most popular crossword puzzle subject is the Bible.

QUIZ ANSWER: Nth (as in the Nth degree)

SEPTEMBER 5th

TODAY'S THOUGHT: "Realtors are people who did not make it as used-car salesmen." —*Bob Newhart*

HISTORY: On this date in 1698 Russian men had a close shave with higher taxes as the government placed a levy on beards.

QUIZ: Which of the following did not, at one time or another, work on a daytime soap?

A: Robert DeNiro   D: Alec Baldwin
B: Kathleen Turner   E: Larry Hagman
C: Wilford Brimley

Trivia
Bob Newhart's real first name is George.

QUIZ ANSWER: C

SEPTEMBER 6th

TODAY'S THOUGHT: "Never invest your money in anything that eats or needs repairing." —*Billy Rose*

HISTORY: On this date in 1620 the Mayflower set sail from Plymouth, England carrying 103 Pilgrims.

QUIZ: What is the daily consumption of mouthwash in the U.S.?

A: 700 gallons   C: 70,000 gallons
B: 7,000 gallons   D: 700,000 gallons

Trivia
Early American colonists made gray paint for their homes by boiling blueberries in milk.

QUIZ ANSWER: C — There's a whole lot of gargling going on as Americans chase away bad breath with about 70,000 gallons daily.

SEPTEMBER 7th

TODAY'S THOUGHT: "Guys are like dogs. They keep comin' back. Ladies are like cats. Yell at a cat one time, they're gone." —*Lenny Bruce*

HISTORY: On this date in 1921 16-year old Margaret Gorman of Washington, D.C. won the first Miss America Pageant.

QUIZ: Bathroom Brain Teaser: If a man was born in 50 B.C., in what year would he celebrate his 100th birthday?

Trivia

Just how fast is a snail's pace? About 25 feet per hour for most species.

QUIZ ANSWER: 51 A.D.

SEPTEMBER 8th

TODAY'S THOUGHT: "When you are courting a nice girl an hour seems like a second. When you sit on a red-hot cinder a second seems like an hour. That's relativity." —*Albert Einstein*

HISTORY: On this date in 1974 an unconditional pardon to Richard Nixon was granted by President Gerald Ford for all federal crimes that he "committed or may have committed" while president.

QUIZ: What is the world's northernmost capital?

Trivia

Electric fans actually increase the temperature of the air.

QUIZ ANSWER: Reykjavik, Iceland

SEPTEMBER 9th

TODAY'S THOUGHT: "There is something supremely reassuring about television: the worst is always yet to come." —*Jack Gould*

HISTORY: On this date in 1956 Elvis Presley sprang upon a largely unsuspecting public on the "Ed Sullivan Show".

QUIZ: What distinction does radio station WHB in Kansas City hold?

Trivia
Tiny earthworms have five hearts.

QUIZ ANSWER: WHB was the first radio station to go to an all rock 'n' roll format.

SEPTEMBER 10th

TODAY'S THOUGHT: "Thanks to the interstate highway system, it is now possible to travel across the country from coast to coast without seeing anything."
—*Charles Kuralt*

HISTORY: On this date in 1846 the world was soon to be in stitches as Elias Howe received a patent on his sewing machine.

QUIZ: Leapin' Lizards! What did Gary Stewart of Ohio do 177,737 times to set a record in California on May 25-26, 1992?

Trivia
There are 170,000,000,000,000,000,000,000,000 ways to play the ten opening moves in a chess game.

QUIZ ANSWER: He bounced on a pogo stick.

SEPTEMBER 11th

TODAY'S THOUGHT: "I consider exercise vulgar. It makes people smell." —*Alec Yuill Thornton*

HISTORY: On this date in 1847 Stephen Foster sold the rights to "Oh, Susanna" to a bartender for a bottle of whiskey so he could celebrate the song's first public performance.

QUIZ: Which Hollywood screen actress once designed a torpedo guidance system for the U.S. Navy?

Trivia
There are five counties in Texas that are larger than the state of Rhode Island.

QUIZ ANSWER: Hedy Lamarr

SEPTEMBER 12th

TODAY'S THOUGHT: "Why is it that men who can go through severe accidents, air raids, and any other major crisis always seem to think they are at death's door when they have a simple head cold?"
—*Shirley Booth*

HISTORY: On this date in 1976 53-year old Minnie Minoso of the Chicago White Sox became the oldest player in Major League baseball history to get a hit in a game.

QUIZ: Name the only X-rated movie to win a Best Picture Oscar.

Trivia
The geographic center of the U.S. is located near Castle Rock, South Dakota.

QUIZ ANSWER: "Midnight Cowboy", starring Dustin Hoffman and Jon Voight

SEPTEMBER 13th

TODAY'S THOUGHT: "Bargain: something you can't use at a price you can't resist." —*Franklin P. Jonas*

HISTORY: On this date in 1971 a 30-year old U.S. Marine captain, Wayne Rollings, stationed in Hawaii, did 17,000 sit-ups in 7 hours, 27 minutes.

QUIZ: If you add up all those between beat rests that your heart takes in the course of a lifetime, you will find that your heart stands still for:

A: about 9 months   D: 8 years
B: 2-1/4 years   E: 20 years
C: 5 years

Trivia
Coca-Cola was banned from India in 1977 for refusing to disclose its secret formula.

QUIZ ANSWER: E — for twenty years

SEPTEMBER 14th

TODAY'S THOUGHT: "I enjoy convalescence. It is the part that makes the illness worthwhile."
—*George Bernard Shaw*

HISTORY: On this date in 1814 Francis Scott Key wrote the words to the national anthem. The melody of "The Star-Spangled Banner" comes from an old English drinking song, "Anachreon in Heaven".

QUIZ: What do the British call tic-tac-toe?

Trivia
Heart attacks claim the fewest men on Fridays.

QUIZ ANSWER: Noughts and crosses

SEPTEMBER 15th

TODAY'S THOUGHT: "An archaeologist is the best husband any woman can have: The older she gets, the more interested he is in her." —*Agatha Christie*

HISTORY: On this date in 1971 the environmental organization, Greenpeace, was founded in Vancouver, British Columbia.

QUIZ: True or False? Chewing gum was initially intended to be a rubber substitute.

Trivia
You use 72 muscles to speak one word.

QUIZ ANSWER: True — Santa Ana tried to sell chicle to the U.S. as a rubber substitute but Thomas Adams got the idea to sell it as chewing gum.

SEPTEMBER 16th

TODAY'S THOUGHT: "I can't take a well-tanned person seriously." —*Cleveland Amory*

HISTORY: On this date in 1630 the little town of Shawmut, Massachusetts decided to change its name to Boston, and it's "bean" that ever since.

QUIZ: When John Kennedy was president of the United States in the early 1960's, there was another John Kennedy who was a Senator in Washington and who, coincidentally, had the same birthday as JFK, May 29. Do you remember him?

Trivia
Teflon was called "fluon" when it was first discovered in 1938.

QUIZ ANSWER: John Kennedy was a third baseman for the Washington Senators baseball club.

SEPTEMBER 17th

TODAY'S THOUGHT: "How many of those dead animals you see on the highway are suicides?"
—*Dennis Miller*

HISTORY: On this date in 1911 C.P. Rogers began the first transcontinental airplane flight from New York to Pasadena. It wasn't exactly a non-stop express; it took over 82 hours.

QUIZ: Can you name the two dogs who have stars on Hollywood's Walk of Fame?

Trivia

Olive Oyl's measurements are 19-19-19.

QUIZ ANSWER: Lassie and Rin Tin Tin

SEPTEMBER 18th

TODAY'S THOUGHT: "At 50, everyone has the face he deserves." —*George Orwell*

HISTORY: On this date in 1947 the United States Air Force took off into the wild blue yonder as it became a separate military service.

QUIZ: How did the blazer jacket come into fashion?

Trivia

The Federal Government forbids the portrait of any living person to appear on a U.S. postage stamp.

QUIZ ANSWER: The captain of the *HMS Blazer* grew tired of seeing his crew shabbily attired so he had blue jackets made for all of them. The fashion caught on and was named after the vessel.

SEPTEMBER 19th

TODAY'S THOUGHT: "Never tell a woman that you didn't realize she was pregnant until you're certain that she is." —*Dave Barry*

HISTORY: On this date in 1928 the first sound cartoon, "Steamboat Willie", debuted at New York's Colony Theater and launched the career of Mickey Mouse.

QUIZ: Bathroom Brain Teaser: In what order are the numbers below?

8   5   4   9   1   7   6   3   2   0

Trivia

The most popular color in the U.S. is blue but the most popular car and house color is white.

QUIZ ANSWER: Alphabetical order

SEPTEMBER 20th

TODAY'S THOUGHT: "A woman's dress should be like a barbed-wire fence: serving its purpose without obstructing the view." —*Sophia Loren*

HISTORY: On this date in 1973 Bobby Riggs was forced to close his mouth after Billie Jean King whipped him in three straight sets in the great Battle of the Sexes tennis match.

QUIZ: What is the best selling children's book in history?

Trivia

Every time Joan Crawford got a divorce she changed toilet seats.

QUIZ ANSWER: "The Tale of Peter Rabbit", by Beatrix Potter

SEPTEMBER 21st

TODAY'S THOUGHT: "Advertising is legalized lying."
—*H.G. Wells*

HISTORY: On this date in 1989 Hurricane Hugo slammed into the southeast coast of the U.S., causing billions of dollars of lost profits for insurance companies.

QUIZ: What First Lady of the United States carried a loaded revolver in her purse?

A: Rachel Jackson   C: Jackie Kennedy
B: Eleanor Roosevelt   D: Nancy Reagan

Trivia
Bela Lugosi is buried in his black Dracula cape.

QUIZ ANSWER: B — After receiving numerous death threats, the Secret Service advised her to carry a gun.

SEPTEMBER 22nd

TODAY'S THOUGHT: "They have Dial-a-Prayer for atheists now. You can call up and it rings and rings and nobody answers." —*Tommy Blaze*

HISTORY: On this date in 1789 the United States Post Office was established.

QUIZ: Name the five U.S. presidents who had beards.

Trivia
John Tyler was the father of fifteen children — so why did they call George Washington the "Father of Our Country"?

QUIZ ANSWER: The five are Abraham Lincoln, Ulysses Grant, Rutherford B. Hayes, James Garfield and Benjamin Harrison.

SEPTEMBER 23rd

TODAY'S THOUGHT: "You always pass failure on the way to success." —*Mickey Rooney*

HISTORY: On this date in 1952 Richard Nixon made his famous "Checkers" speech, in which he vowed not to return his beloved cocker spaniel which had been a gift to his daughters from some political supporters.

QUIZ: Name the following presidents' pooches.

A: Lyndon Johnson   C: Dwight Eisenhower

B: George Bush   D: Ronald Reagan

Trivia

The most common noncontagious disease is tooth decay.

QUIZ ANSWER: A — He and She; B — Millie;
C — Heidi; D — Rex and Lucky

SEPTEMBER 24th

TODAY'S THOUGHT: "Last night I dreamt I had insomnia. When I woke up, I was completely exhausted but too well rested to go back to sleep."
—*Bob Nickman*

HISTORY: On this date in 1934 Babe Ruth played his last game for the Yankees and bid farewell to his fans at Yankee Stadium.

QUIZ: On what day is Superman's birthday?

Trivia

In eight years a male greyhound in London sired 2,414 registered puppies as well as 600 others that weren't registered.

QUIZ ANSWER: February 29

SEPTEMBER 25th

TODAY'S THOUGHT: "You know you're getting old when you stoop to tie your shoes and wonder what else you can do while you're down there." —*George Burns*

HISTORY: On this date in 1981 Sandra Day O'Connor was sworn in as the first female Justice of the Supreme Court.

QUIZ: They say "break a leg" in show biz, but Jack Palance, Edward G. Robinson, Ann-Margret, Montgomery Clift and Jason Robards Jr. have something else in common. Do you know what it is?

Trivia
A cat's sense of smell is ten times better than a human's.

QUIZ ANSWER: They have all been in serious accidents that required facial reconstructive surgery.

SEPTEMBER 26th

TODAY'S THOUGHT: "Marriage is a wonderful institution. But who would want to live in an institution?" —*H.L. Mencken*

HISTORY: On this date in 1969 the Beatles thirteenth and final album, "Abbey Road", was released.

QUIZ: Olivia Newton-John wasn't the first in her family to be famous. Who was her illustrious ancestor?

Trivia
T.S. Eliot's favorite gift to critics was exploding cigars.

QUIZ ANSWER: Her grandfather was one of the greatest scientists of the century, Nobel Prize winner Max Born.

SEPTEMBER 27th

TODAY'S THOUGHT: "If you die in an elevator, be sure to press the UP button." —*Sam Levenson*

HISTORY: On this date in 1964 the Warren Commission issued its endlessly debated report that Lee Harvey Oswald acted alone in the assassination of President Kennedy.

QUIZ: Where is bowling's Hall of Fame located?
A: Newport, RI B: St. Louis, MO C: Pinehurst, NC

Trivia

The first bathroom to be installed in a U.S. residence was in the Vanderbuilt home in New York in 1855.

QUIZ ANSWER: B

SEPTEMBER 28th

TODAY'S THOUGHT: "People always say 'He died penniless', as if it's a terrible thing. Sounds like good timing to me." —*Al Cleathen*

HISTORY: On this date in 1960 Ted Williams wound up his career by hitting a home run, his 521st, in his very last at-bat.

QUIZ: Try "Taxi"ing your brain and name the cab company in the television series "Taxi".

Trivia

Confucius was not always a famous philosopher; at age seventeen he was a corn inspector at the markets.

QUIZ ANSWER: The Sunshine Taxi Company

SEPTEMBER 29th

TODAY'S THOUGHT: "If there is a God, give me a sign!... See, I told you that the knlupt smflrt glpptnrr..."
—*Steve Martin*

HISTORY: On this date in 1983 "A Chorus Line" staged its 3,389th performance, thus becoming the longest running show in Broadway history.

QUIZ: How many millions are in a trillion?

Trivia
The goldfish has a life span of 25 years.

QUIZ ANSWER: One million (A thousand millions make a billion and one thousand billions make a trillion.)

SEPTEMBER 30th

TODAY'S THOUGHT: "If life was fair, Elvis would be alive and all the impersonators would be dead."
—*Johnny Carson*

HISTORY: On this date in 1911 Lt. H.H. Arnold became the first stuntman while performing dangerous feats for the film "The Military Air Scout".

QUIZ: Bathroom Brain Teaser: If you drive a bus from New York to Philadelphia with 40 people on board, and drop off 4 people at six different stops and pick up 5 people at each of these stops, when you get to Philadelphia three hours later, what is the driver's name?

Trivia
The second man to walk on the lunar surface was Buzz Aldrin. His mother's maiden name is Moon.

QUIZ ANSWER: Your name

OCTOBER 1st

TODAY'S THOUGHT: "Be nice to your children, for they will choose your rest home." —*Phyllis Diller*

HISTORY: On this date in 1971 Disney World opened in Orlando, Florida.

QUIZ: What's the only state in the U.S. that ends in "k"?

Trivia

The largest single edition of a newspaper was the "New York Times", dated Sunday, October 10, 1971. There were fifteen sections with a total of 972 pages; each copy weighed over seven pounds.

QUIZ ANSWER: New York

OCTOBER 2nd

TODAY'S THOUGHT: "Politics is the art of looking for trouble, finding it everywhere, diagnosing it incorrectly and applying the wrong remedies." —*Groucho Marx*

HISTORY: On this date in 1959 Rod Serling first beckoned Americans into the "Twilight Zone".

QUIZ: Which came first, Coke or Pepsi?

Trivia

Most trips taken in the U.S. by car are under five miles.

QUIZ ANSWER: Coca-Cola was introduced in 1896. Pepsi followed ten years later.

OCTOBER 3rd

TODAY'S THOUGHT: "I wish people who have trouble communicating would just shut up." —*Tom Lehrer*

HISTORY: On this date in 1955 Annette slapped on her first pair of giant ears as "The Mickey Mouse Club" hit the airwaves. Remember Roy on the show? Besides appearing on camera he also wrote the theme song.

QUIZ: Who did Johnny and the Moondogs eventually become?

Trivia
The average person loses 50-100 strands of hair every day.

QUIZ ANSWER: They went on to become the Foreverly Brothers and the Moonshiners, the Quarrymen Skiffle Group and finally, the Beatles.

OCTOBER 4th

TODAY'S THOUGHT: "It costs a lot of money to look this cheap." —*Dolly Parton*

HISTORY: On this date in 1957 Wally and the Beav first shuffled into America's living rooms as "Leave It to Beaver" debuted on TV.

QUIZ: Can you guess the celebrities who go with these given names?

A: Aaron Chwatt   D: John Elroy Sanford
B: Nathan Birnbaum   E: Paul Reubenfeld
C: Nicholas Coppola

Trivia
75% of optometrists wear eyeglasses.

QUIZ ANSWER: A — Red Buttons; B — George Burns; C — Nicholas Cage (and yes, he is related); D — Redd Foxx; E — Pee Wee Herman

The Bathroom Trivia Almanac

OCTOBER 5th

TODAY'S THOUGHT: "Van Gogh became a painter because he had no ear for music." —*Nikki Harris*

HISTORY: On this date in 1921 Graham McNamee took to the radio airwaves to broadcast the first play-by-play coverage of a World Series game.

QUIZ: Are forts your forte? Match the following with their location.

1 — Fort Ticonderoga   A: Pittsburgh, PA
2 — Fort Sumter   B: Wyoming
3 — Fort Laramie   C: New York
4 — Fort Duquesne   D: Charleston, SC

Trivia
An elephant grows six sets of teeth during a lifetime.

QUIZ ANSWER: 1 — C; 2 — D; 3 — B; 4 — A

OCTOBER 6th

TODAY'S THOUGHT: "We must believe in luck. For how else can we explain the success of those we don't like?" —*Jean Cocteau*

HISTORY: On this date in 1863 the first Turkish bath opened in Brooklyn, operated by Dr. C.H. Sheperd. You could take a bath there for $1, considerably cheaper than taking a bath on Wall Street.

QUIZ: What is the official language of Greenland?

Trivia
The average American generates three pounds of garbage a day.

QUIZ ANSWER: Danish

OCTOBER 7th

TODAY'S THOUGHT: "The reason grandparents and grandchildren get along so well is that they have a common enemy." —*Sam Levenson*

HISTORY: On this date in 1916 the greatest rout ever to take place on the gridiron was played as Georgia Tech whipped Cumberland University 222-0.

QUIZ: Which is the only one of the Seven Wonders of the Ancient World still in existence?

Trivia

Not to rain on your parade, but there are over one quadrillion ants living on the planet.

QUIZ ANSWER: The Sphinx

OCTOBER 8th

TODAY'S THOUGHT: "Never look down on anybody unless you're helping him up." —*Jesse Jackson*

HISTORY: On this date in 1871 Mrs. O'Leary's cow turned the tables on would-be barbecuers as it began the Great Chicago Fire which virtually destroyed the city.

QUIZ: Which president is credited with making Thanksgiving an official holiday?

Trivia

Eddie Rickenbacker raced in the first five Indy 500 races before becoming a WWI flying ace.

QUIZ ANSWER: Abe Lincoln proclaimed the last Thursday in November be celebrated back in 1863.

OCTOBER 9th

TODAY'S THOUGHT: "Will the people in the cheaper seats clap your hands? All the rest of you, if you'll just rattle your jewelry." —*John Lennon*

HISTORY: On this date in 1888 the Washington Monument opened.

QUIZ: True or False? Pittsburgh, Pennsylvania is farther east than Miami, Florida.

Trivia

When NBC plays three musical notes with its logo on TV, those notes are "G — E — C" for the General Electric Corporation which owns the network.

QUIZ ANSWER: True

OCTOBER 10th

TODAY'S THOUGHT: "Somewhere on this globe, every ten seconds there is a woman giving birth to a child. She must be found and stopped." —*Sam Levenson*

HISTORY: On this date in 1886 Griswold Lorillard showed up at the Autumn Ball at the Tuxedo Park Country Club, New York positively resplendent, decked out in the first formal dinner jacket. He was the talk of the town and the name tuxedo stuck.

QUIZ: Where is the only place the United States flag is flown at full staff 24 hours a day, 365 days a year without ever being raised, lowered or saluted?

Trivia

Last names in China are always one syllable.

QUIZ ANSWER: The moon

OCTOBER 11th

TODAY'S THOUGHT: "I have nothing to say and I am saying it." —*John Cage*

HISTORY: On this date in 1950 the FCC granted CBS permission to start broadcasting selected TV shows in color.

QUIZ: What two words in the English language end in "gry"?

Trivia
For 186 days a year, the sun is not seen at the North Pole.

QUIZ ANSWER: Hungry and angry

OCTOBER 12th

TODAY'S THOUGHT: "If you come to a fork in the road, take it." —*Yogi Berra*

HISTORY: On this date in 1792 the first celebration of Columbus took place, on the 300th anniversary of Columbus' expedition.

QUIZ: During the Civil War, were there any slave states that remained part of the Union?

Trivia
Lettuce is the world's most popular green.

QUIZ ANSWER: Yes, they were Delaware, Maryland, Kentucky and Missouri.

OCTOBER 13th

TODAY'S THOUGHT: "People want to know why I do this, why I write such gross stuff. I like to tell them I have the heart of a small boy and I keep it in a jar on my desk." —*Stephen King*

HISTORY: On this date in 1792 the cornerstone of the White House was laid.

QUIZ: What famous sixties musical act was known in the fifties as Tom and Jerry?

Trivia
Henry VIII had Sir Nicholas Carew beheaded because he bested him in a bowling match.

QUIZ ANSWER: Tom and Jerry later became somewhat more famous as Simon and Garfunkel.

OCTOBER 14th

TODAY'S THOUGHT: "I'm not bald — I'm just taller than my hair." —*Thom Sharpe*

HISTORY: On this date in 1917 France executed one Margaretha Zelle for her activities on behalf of Germany. History knows her as Mata Hari.

QUIZ: True or False? The term "meatless Mondays" referred to Catholicism's abstinence from meat until 1960 when Pope John XXIII changed the day to "fish Fridays".

Trivia
West Point originated class rings.

QUIZ ANSWER: False — "Meatless Mondays" originated during World War I when Americans were urged not to eat meat on that day in order to conserve food for the war.

OCTOBER 15th

TODAY'S THOUGHT: "I don't want any yes-men around me. I want everyone to tell me the truth even if it costs them their jobs." —*Samuel Goldwyn*

HISTORY: On this date in 1951 "I Love Lucy" debuted on CBS.

QUIZ: What two geographical records are held by Inyo County, California?

Trivia
The U.S. would fit into the African continent three times.

QUIZ ANSWER: Both the highest and lowest spots in the continental United States are found within that county and only 86 miles apart. Mount Whitney is 14,495 feet above sea level while Death Valley is 276 feet below sea level.

OCTOBER 16th

TODAY'S THOUGHT: "A form of ugliness so intolerable that we have to alter it every six months."
—*Oscar Wilde, on fashion*

HISTORY: On this date in 1793 Marie "Let them eat cake" Antoinette was beheaded.

QUIZ: In the poem "Casey at the Bat", who was Mudville's opponent and what was the final score of the game?

Trivia
Oscar Wilde's last words were, "This wallpaper is killing me; one of us has to go."

QUIZ ANSWER: The Mudville Nine lost to an anonymous team, 4-2.

OCTOBER 17th

TODAY'S THOUGHT: "I never worry about diets. The only carrots that interest me are the number you get in a diamond." —*Mae West*

HISTORY: On this date in 1989 the World Series was delayed by an earthquake measuring 7.1 on the Richter Scale as it rocked Candlestick Park and the San Francisco Bay area.

QUIZ: If you are dining in England and order broccoli, what will you get?

Trivia

Buckingham Palace is the former site of a brothel.

QUIZ ANSWER: Cauliflower

OCTOBER 18th

TODAY'S THOUGHT: "All pro athletes are bilingual. They speak English and profanity." —*Gordie Howe*

HISTORY: On this date in 1869 "Seward's Folly" was consummated as the United States took possession of Alaska from the Russians.

QUIZ: In a standard deck of playing cards, which one of the four kings is shown in profile?

Trivia

Johnny Unitas threw at least one touchdown pass in 47 consecutive games.

QUIZ ANSWER: The king of diamonds

OCTOBER 19th

TODAY'S THOUGHT: "There is no shortage of lawyers in Washington, D.C. In fact, there may be more lawyers than people." —*Sandra Day O'Connor*

HISTORY: On this date in 1781 Cornwallis surrendered to Washington at Yorktown, effectively ending the Revolutionary War.

QUIZ: Backward thinking is required for this one. What do the words uncomplimentary, unnoticeably and subcontinental have in common?

Trivia

J. Edgar Hoover would not allow anyone to walk on his shadow.

QUIZ ANSWER: They all have the vowels a-e-i-o-u in reverse order.

OCTOBER 20th

TODAY'S THOUGHT: "The older I get, the less important the comma becomes. Let the reader catch his own breath." —*Elizabeth Clarkson Zwart*

HISTORY: On this date in 1944 General Douglas MacArthur proved to be a man of his word as he and thousands of his troops returned to the Philippines.

QUIZ: What 492 foot long memorial did Yale student Maya Ying Lin design?

Trivia

Albert Einstein was four years old before he could talk.

QUIZ ANSWER: The Vietnam Veterans Memorial in Washington, D.C.

OCTOBER 21st

TODAY'S THOUGHT: "To my embarrassment, I was born in bed with a lady." —*Wilson Mizner*

HISTORY: On this date in 1879 Edison's brightest idea came to light as he invented the first practical incandescent electric light bulb.

QUIZ: Which dam is on the Colorado River between Nevada and Arizona, the Hoover Dam or the Boulder Dam?

Trivia
The average American adult male is 5 feet 9.1 inches tall. The average woman is 5 feet 3.7 inches tall.

QUIZ ANSWER: They are the same dam thing. Erected from 1931-1936, the Hoover (or Boulder) Dam is over 700 feet high and 1,200 feet long.

OCTOBER 22nd

TODAY'S THOUGHT: "A baby boomer is a man who hires someone to cut the grass so he can play golf for exercise." —*Anonymous*

HISTORY: On this date in 1962 President Kennedy took to television to demand that the Soviets remove their missiles from Cuba.

QUIZ: What ups and downs might be found at 165 Eaton Place in London?

Trivia
George Washington gave the shortest presidential inaugural address at his second inaugural—135 words.

QUIZ ANSWER: That was the address of the house in the PBS series "Upstairs, Downstairs".

OCTOBER 23rd

TODAY'S THOUGHT: "My husband thinks that health food is anything he eats before the expiration date."
—Rita Rudner

HISTORY: On this date in 1962 twelve-year old Stevie Wonder made his first recording, "Thank You for Loving Me All the Way", for Motown.

QUIZ: Bathroom Brain Teaser: September 9, 1981 (9/9/81) marked the last time in the 20th century that the product of the month times the day equaled the last two digits of the year (9 x 9 = 81). When's the first time this will happen in the 21st century?

Trivia
A year contains 31,557,600 seconds.

QUIZ ANSWER: It already happened- 2,001 (1/1/01)

OCTOBER 24th

TODAY'S THOUGHT: "Life is like a dogsled team. If you ain't the lead dog, the scene never changes."
—Lewis Grizzard

HISTORY: On this date in 1826 the patent was issued for an invention that never set the world on fire, the safety match.

QUIZ: An Oklahoma City journalist named Carl Magee invented it. The first one was installed at the intersection of First Street and Robinson in July, 1935. What is it?

Trivia
China's Zeng Jinlian was the world's tallest woman at eight feet, two inches.

QUIZ ANSWER: A parking meter

OCTOBER 25th

TODAY'S THOUGHT: "People will accept your idea much more readily if you tell them Benjamin Franklin said it first." —*David H. Comins*

HISTORY: On this date in 1972 the first female FBI agents completed their training in Quantico, Virginia.

QUIZ: What unusual quality do the names of the first five presidents have in common?

Trivia
The term "potty" dates back to when England had chamber pots and made kid-sized pots.

QUIZ ANSWER: George Washington, John Adams, Thomas Jefferson, James Madison and James Monroe had no middle names.

OCTOBER 26th

TODAY'S THOUGHT: "I got the bill for my surgery. Now I know what those three doctors are wearing masks for." —*James H. Boren*

HISTORY: On this date in 1881 the Earp brothers and Doc Holliday defeated the Clanton boys at the OK Corral in Tombstone, Arizona.

QUIZ: What famous child actress auditioned for a regular part in the "Our Gang" comedies in the early thirties but was turned down flat?

Trivia
The soy bean is the most versatile vegetable on earth with 400 different products made with it.

QUIZ ANSWER: Shirley Temple

OCTOBER 27th

TODAY'S THOUGHT: "If you shoot a mime, should you use a silencer?" —*Steven Wright*

HISTORY: On this date in 1977 Anwar Sadat and Menachem Begin received the Nobel Peace Prize.

QUIZ: Who signed off with the following:
A: "Peace."
B: "And that's the way it is."
C: "Good night and good news."
D: "Good night and may God bless."

Trivia
The most likely magazine to be stolen from a U.S. public library is "Sports Illustrated".

QUIZ ANSWER: A — Dave Garroway; B — Walter Cronkite; C — Ted Baxter; D — Red Skelton

OCTOBER 28th

TODAY'S THOUGHT: "Your dresses should be tight enough to show you're a woman and loose enough to show you're a lady." —*Edith Head*

HISTORY: On this date in 1886 the Statue of Liberty was dedicated on Bedloe's Island. The inscription "Give me your tired, your poor, your huddled masses..." was written by Emma Lazarus.

QUIZ: How many M&M's colors are there?

Trivia
The only U.S. landmark that moves around is the fabled cable cars in San Francisco.

QUIZ ANSWER: Seven — blue, brown, green, orange, red, tan and yellow

OCTOBER 29th

TODAY'S THOUGHT: "Money won't buy happiness, but it will pay the salaries of a large research staff to study the problem." —*Bill Vaughan*

HISTORY: On this date in 1929 the Great Depression began as the stock market collapsed, putting many companies out of business and causing economic chaos which lasted until WWII.

QUIZ: What do the initials stand for in L.L. Cool J.'s name?

Trivia

Delaware has the highest concentration of millionaires of any state.

QUIZ ANSWER: The initial laden monicker stands for "Ladies Love Cool James".

OCTOBER 30th

TODAY'S THOUGHT: "At my age, I don't even buy green bananas." —*George Burns*

HISTORY: On this date in 1938 Orson Welles and the Mercury Players scared the pants off America with their Halloween Eve broadcast of "The War of the Worlds".

QUIZ: What did Germany offer England at the end of World War II as part of their reparations?

Trivia

John Adams, George Washington and Thomas Jefferson were avid marble collectors and players.

QUIZ ANSWER: The Volkswagen business—Those savvy English politicians turned it down, figuring that no one would ever want a car with such high gas mileage and an engine in the rear.

OCTOBER 31st

TODAY'S THOUGHT: "This country is so urbanized we think low-fat milk comes from cows on aerobic exercise programs." —*P.J. O'Rourke*

HISTORY: On this date in 1926 magician Harry Houdini died.

QUIZ: Why do the palms of your hands and the soles of your feet wrinkle when immersed in water?

Trivia

Every clown is unique. Their faces have to be painted on an eggshell to be registered. When a clown dies, his egg is buried with him, no doubt sunny-side up.

QUIZ ANSWER: Because those areas have no oil glands, and therefore no protective oil, the skin becomes waterlogged.

NOVEMBER 1st

TODAY'S THOUGHT: "You know the problem with men? After the birth, we're irrelevant."
—*Dustin Hoffman*

HISTORY: On this date in 1939 Rudolph the Red-Nosed Reindeer first appeared in a pamphlet given away as a holiday promotion at a Chicago store. Rudy has since gone on to star in numerous specials, books, movies and even the second best-selling song of all time.

QUIZ: Can you name the oldest fast-food hamburger chain?

Trivia

The lobster automatically acquires a new form fitting shell every year.

QUIZ ANSWER: White Castle, which opened in 1921

NOVEMBER 2nd

TODAY'S THOUGHT: "Jogging is very beneficial. It's good for your legs and your feet. It's also very good for the ground. It makes it feel needed." —*Snoopy*

HISTORY: On this date in 1948 Harry Truman confounded pundits and embarrassed newspaper headline writers by defeating Dewey.

QUIZ: Here is one to numb your noggin; you almost surely have the answer in your head; it's just a matter of retrieving it. What national retail chain doesn't use cash registers at all?

Trivia

Ted Kennedy's middle name is Moore.

QUIZ ANSWER: Radio Shack — They use a computer to record the details of the sale and make change out of a separate cash drawer.

NOVEMBER 3rd

TODAY'S THOUGHT: "The only real way to look younger is not to be born so soon." —*Charles Schulz*

HISTORY: On this date in 1992 Arkansas Governor Bill Clinton was elected 42nd President of the United States. Clinton garnered 370 electoral votes in his victory over George Bush and Ross Perot.

QUIZ: True or False? Election Day falls on the first Tuesday of November.

Trivia
One jelly bean has seven calories.

QUIZ ANSWER: False — It occurs on the first Tuesday after the first Monday of November.

NOVEMBER 4th

TODAY'S THOUGHT: "If God didn't want man to hunt, he wouldn't have given us plaid shirts."
—*Johnny Carson*

HISTORY: On this date in 1922 King Tut's tomb was discovered by Harold Carter at Luxor, Egypt.

QUIZ: What is the one thing that creditors can't take away from you if you go bankrupt? (Hint: You must be married.)

Trivia
William Phelps Eno invented the one-way street.

QUIZ ANSWER: Your wedding ring

NOVEMBER 5th

TODAY'S THOUGHT: "One disadvantage of having nothing to do is you can't stop and rest."
—*Franklin P. Jones*

HISTORY: On this date in 1781 the first president of the United States was elected. It was not George Washington but John Hanson of Maryland. His official title was "President of the United States in Congress Assembled". He served for over a year and had six successors before Washington took over.

QUIZ: What's the first name of golf's Tiger Woods?

Trivia
It took Abe Lincoln all of two minutes to deliver his Gettysburg Address.

QUIZ ANSWER: Eldrick

NOVEMBER 6th

TODAY'S THOUGHT: "Prayer never seems to work for me on the golf course. I think it has something to do with me being a terrible putter." —*Billy Graham*

HISTORY: On this date in 1860 Abraham Lincoln was elected president; in 1888 it was Benjamin Harrison; in 1900 William McKinley was elected; in 1928 Herbert Hoover was the victor.

QUIZ: Is there any place in nature where alligators and crocodiles live together?

Trivia
Elephants can swim very well. They just have trouble keeping their trunks up.

QUIZ ANSWER: Only one place, southern Florida — But don't be expecting little crocogators or tiny allidiles; they don't socialize that much.

NOVEMBER 7th

TODAY'S THOUGHT: "Our language is funny —
a fat chance and slim chance are the same thing."
—*J. Gustav White*

HISTORY: On this date in 1962 Richard Nixon held his
"last" press conference, having just lost the California
gubernatorial race. He thus uttered one of the most
ironic lines in the history of American politics, "You
won't have Dick Nixon to kick around any more!"

QUIZ: What's the only land or sea animal that can turn
its stomach inside out?

Trivia
*The weekly magazine with the highest circulation is "TV
Guide" which averages nineteen million copies a week.*

QUIZ ANSWER: The starfish, enabling it to eat its prey

NOVEMBER 8th

TODAY'S THOUGHT: "Death and taxes and childbirth!
There's never any convenient time for any of them!"
—*Margaret Mitchell*

HISTORY: On this date in 1970 Tom Dempsey
of the New Orleans Saints kicked a record field goal
of 63 yards.

QUIZ: What famous composer's wife helped invent the
johnny mop?

Trivia
Most people put on their left sock first.

QUIZ ANSWER: Richard Rodgers (His wife's name was
Dorothy.)

NOVEMBER 9th

TODAY'S THOUGHT: "An intellectual is a man who doesn't know how to park a bike." —*Spiro Agnew*

HISTORY: On this date in 1989 the first crack in the Berlin Wall appeared as East Germany opened many of the checkpoints in the barrier and, after 28 years, allowed its citizens to come and go.

QUIZ: Spiro Agnew resigned from the vice-presidency of the U.S. on October 10, 1973. Richard Nixon resigned from the presidency less than a year later, on August 9, 1974. Who replaced Agnew and who replaced Nixon?

Trivia

The four least used letters of the alphabet, in order of their infrequency, are Q, X, Z and J.

QUIZ ANSWER: Gerald Ford replaced both of them.

NOVEMBER 10th

TODAY'S THOUGHT: "Ninety-eight percent of the adults in this country are decent, hard working, honest Americans. It's the other lousy two percent that get all the publicity. But then — we elected them."
—*Lily Tomlin*

HISTORY: On this date in 1871 Henry Stanley found David Livingstone in Tanganyika and uttered his famous greeting, "Dr. Livingstone, I presume."

QUIZ: What sports "first" belongs to Diane Crump?

Trivia

Those symbols that cartoonists draw to replace epithets are called dingbats.

QUIZ ANSWER: Diane Crump was the first female (human, anyway) to participate in the Kentucky Derby.

NOVEMBER 11th

TODAY'S THOUGHT: "Most people don't care about authors. It's like being in a Lacrosse Hall of Fame. I call up almost any office and have to spell my name."
—*Kurt Vonnegut*

HISTORY: On this date in 1939 Kate Smith first sang "God Bless America" on television.

QUIZ: True or False? "Oklahoma" is the official state song of Oklahoma.

Trivia

Do you flush the toilet while sitting on it? One out of every three Americans does.

QUIZ ANSWER: True

NOVEMBER 12th

TODAY'S THOUGHT: "Remember when you used to watch TV in the sixties and you'd see Perry Como in a cashmere sweater? That's what rock 'n' roll is becoming. It's your parents' music." —*Neil Young*

HISTORY: On this date in 1892 professional football had its modest start as William "Pudge" Heffelfinger became the first pro player, signed by the Allegheny Athletic Association.

QUIZ: The vast majority of people can't answer this question about themselves. What is the largest organ on your body?

Trivia

In ancient Rome, a hooked nose was thought to be a sign of leadership.

QUIZ ANSWER: Your skin

NOVEMBER 13th

TODAY'S THOUGHT: "A race track is a place where windows clean people." —*Danny Thomas*

HISTORY: On this date in 1927 the Holland Tunnel, running under the Hudson River between New York City and Jersey City, NJ opened to traffic.

QUIZ: Craig T. Nelson stars on TV's "Coach" but, before he hit the big time, he knocked around as half of a comedy team. Who was the other half?

Trivia

The median length of a marriage in the U.S. is now just seven years.

QUIZ ANSWER: His partner was Barry Levinson, director of such films as "Diner", "Rain Man" and "Bugsy".

NOVEMBER 14th

TODAY'S THOUGHT: "The average, healthy, well-adjusted adult gets up at seven-thirty in the morning feeling just plain terrible." —*Jean Kerr*

HISTORY: On this date in 1889 Nellie Bly bested Jules Verne's fictional hero, Phileas Fogg, by using ships, trains, camels and dog carts to go around the world in 72 days.

QUIZ: You're probably on "the best seat in the house" right now, but do you know the underwear manufacturer which has used that slogan?

Trivia

548 peanuts are needed to make a 12 ounce jar of peanut butter.

QUIZ ANSWER: Jockey

The Bathroom Trivia Almanac

NOVEMBER 15th

TODAY'S THOUGHT: "Assume nothing. Inside every dumb blond there may be a very smart brunette."
—*Ann Landers*

HISTORY: On this date in 1937 the U.S. Senate and House were air-conditioned but, with all that hot air, the system's been fighting a losing battle ever since!

QUIZ: Who were the mother and daughter who adorned the Ivory Snow box during the sixties?

Trivia
Soupy Sales claims he has been hit with over 19,253 pies during his career. That takes a lot of crust.

QUIZ ANSWER: Not everything was 99-44/100 percent pure. The mother was porn star, Marilyn Chambers, and the daughter was Brooke Shields.

NOVEMBER 16th

TODAY'S THOUGHT: "I guess I wouldn't believe in anything if it wasn't for my lucky astrology mood watch."
—*Steve Martin*

HISTORY: On this date in 1982 the eight week National Football League players' strike ended. It is estimated that the strike cost the parties concerned about 450 million dollars.

QUIZ: Who was Tad Dorgan and why do lovers of true Americana owe this hot dog a great debt?

Trivia
3% of Americans hang family pictures in their bathrooms.

QUIZ ANSWER: He is the man who, in 1905, changed the name of "dachshund sausages" to hot dogs.

NOVEMBER 17th

TODAY'S THOUGHT: "It's funny that women aren't embarrassed when they buy men's pajamas, but a guy purchasing a nightgown acts as though he was making a deal with a dope peddler." —*Anonymous*

HISTORY: On this date in 1956 football great Jim Brown set an NCAA scoring record of 43 points for Syracuse against Colgate University. Brown scored six touchdowns and kicked seven extra points.

QUIZ: Bathroom Brain Teaser: What two things do the words diaper, drawer and spools have in common?

Trivia
A hummingbird lays only two eggs during its lifetime.

QUIZ ANSWER: They are all six letter words and all three spell another word when the lettering is reversed.

NOVEMBER 18th

TODAY'S THOUGHT: "When a man retires and time is no longer a matter of urgent importance, his colleagues usually present him with a watch." —*R.C. Sherriff*

HISTORY: On this date in 1865 Mark Twain's first piece of fiction was published in the "New York Saturday Press". It was called "The Celebrated Jumping Frog of Calaveras County".

QUIZ: See if you can match the city with its nickname:

1 — Akron, OH   A: Fruitbowl of the Nation
2 — Annapolis, MD   B: Nail City
3 — Wheeling, WV   C: Rubber City
4 — Yakima, WA   D: Crabtown

Trivia
Alan Shepard was the first astronaut to play golf on the moon.

QUIZ ANSWER: 1 — C; 2 — D; 3 — B; 4 — A

NOVEMBER 19th

TODAY'S THOUGHT: "If I only had a little humility, I'd be perfect." —*Ted Turner*

HISTORY: On this date in 1861 Julia Ward Howe wrote "The Battle Hymn of the Republic".

QUIZ: What was the name of the horse that Paul Revere took on his midnight ride?

A: Midnight   C: Black Beauty
B: Daylight   D: Brown Beauty

Trivia
A housefly beats its wings an average of 20,000 times a minute.

QUIZ ANSWER: D — Brown Beauty

NOVEMBER 20th

TODAY'S THOUGHT: "Observe your dog; if he's fat you're not getting enough exercise." —*Evan Esar*

HISTORY: On this date in 1888 the first time clock was invented by William Bundy, and a lot of people have wanted to punch him out ever since!

QUIZ: What do Leslie Hornby, Maria Rosario Pilar Martinez, George Joseph Kresge Jr., Gordon Matthew Sumner and Edson Arantes do Nascimento have in common?

Trivia
One out of every ten paper clips is bought by the U.S. government.

QUIZ ANSWER: They are celebrities who changed their monickers to just one name. In order, they are: Twiggy, Charo, Kreskin, Sting and Pele.

NOVEMBER 21st

TODAY'S THOUGHT: "As a nation we are dedicated to keeping physically fit — and parking as close to the stadium as possible." —*Bill Vaughan*

HISTORY: On this date in 1964 the world's longest suspension bridge opened over the Verrazano Narrows between Brooklyn and Staten Island.

QUIZ: Where did television's most defiantly dysfunctional family, "The Simpsons", get their first names?

Trivia
Voltaire drank 70 cups of coffee a day.

QUIZ ANSWER: Those are the names of creator Matt Groening's family, except for Bart which is an anagram of brat.

NOVEMBER 22nd

TODAY'S THOUGHT: "How can you govern a country which has 246 varieties of cheese?" —*Charles de Gaulle*

HISTORY: On this date in 1963 President John F. Kennedy was killed in a motorcade in Dallas.

QUIZ: A look above at this date in history will provide you with a clue to this question. What is located at 506 Elm Street?

Trivia
One-fourth of all the turkey eaten in the U.S. is gobbled down on Thanksgiving Day.

QUIZ ANSWER: The Texas School Book Depository in Dallas, Texas

NOVEMBER 23rd

TODAY'S THOUGHT: "Whenever you want to marry someone, go have lunch with his ex-wife."
—*Shelley Winters*

HISTORY: On this date in 1936 the first issue of "Life" magazine, created by Henry Luce, hit the newsstands.

QUIZ: Who are Matthew Prescott and Alexandra Maitland, and what grounds do they have for their long running TV relationship?

Trivia

Franklin Pierce was once arrested for accidentally running down Mrs. Nathan Lewis while on horseback.

QUIZ ANSWER: They are the Taster's Choice couple, and their caffeine fueled courtship is now the subject of a romance novel entitled "Love Over Gold".

NOVEMBER 24th

TODAY'S THOUGHT: "On Thanksgiving Day all over America, families sit down to dinner at the same moment — halftime." —*Anonymous*

HISTORY: On this date in 1963 Lee Harvey Oswald was shot to death in Dallas, Texas by Jack Ruby.

QUIZ: What do you call a young turkey?

Trivia

The first air mail pilot took off and flew in the wrong direction, thus setting the standard for postal service to this very day.

QUIZ ANSWER: A poult (and a whole lot of them on branches make a poult-tree)

NOVEMBER 25th

TODAY'S THOUGHT: "A ball player's got to be kept hungry to become a big leaguer. That's why no boy from a rich family ever made the big leagues."
—Joe Di Maggio

HISTORY: On this date in 1952 Agatha Christie's "The Mousetrap" opened in London at the Ambassador Theater and is still running.

QUIZ: Two states in the U.S. have names which contain three consecutive vowels. One is Hawaii. Do you know the other?

Trivia
The longest non-scientific word in the dictionary is floccinaucinihilipilification, meaning deciding if something has no value.

QUIZ ANSWER: Louisiana

NOVEMBER 26th

TODAY'S THOUGHT: "I love mankind — it's people I can't stand." —Charles Schulz

HISTORY: On this date in 1832 the first streetcar in the U.S. began its horsedrawn journey between New York's City Hall and 14th Street. The fare was 12-1/2 cents. Many transit delays were encountered as passengers tried to meet the exact change requirement by breaking pennies in half...

QUIZ: By what other name was the National-sozialistische Deustche Arbeiter-Partei known?

Trivia
Hershey, Pennsylvania used to be known as Derry Church. Wonder if Derry Church Bars would ever have caught on?

QUIZ ANSWER: The Nazi Party — The term Nazi is a phonetic spelling of the party's first two syllables.

NOVEMBER 27th

TODAY'S THOUGHT: "When men reach their sixties and retire, they go to pieces. Women just go right on cooking." —*Gail Sheehy*

HISTORY: On this date in 1966 the Washington Redskins defeated the New York Giants, 72-41, in the highest scoring game in NFL history.

QUIZ: Baseball Hall of Famer Frank Robinson and football's Art Shell hold a similar distinction in their respective sports. What is it?

Trivia

At a rate of one drop a minute, a leaking faucet can waste 900 gallons of water a year.

QUIZ ANSWER: Robinson was Major League baseball's first black manager and Shell was NFL's first black head coach.

NOVEMBER 28th

TODAY'S THOUGHT: "I love children, especially when they cry, for then someone takes them away." —*Nancy Mitford*

HISTORY: On this date in 1776 General Washington crossed the Delaware.

QUIZ: What's another name for the aquatic sport of octopush?

Trivia

Every two weeks a lemon shark grows a new set of teeth. That is more than 24,000 new teeth each year.

QUIZ ANSWER: Underwater hockey

NOVEMBER 29th

TODAY'S THOUGHT: "The average dog is a nicer person than the average person." —*Andy Rooney*

HISTORY: On this date in 1872 Horace Greeley died insane only three weeks after losing the U.S. presidential election to Ulysses Grant.

QUIZ: Give the marquee monickers of these folks.

A: Jill Oppenheim   D: Lee Siu Loong
B: Hugh J. Krampe   E: Krishna Bhanji
C: Ivo Montand Livi

Trivia
The butterfly is a cannibal.

QUIZ ANSWER: A — Jill St. John; B — Hugh O'Brian; C — Yves Montand; D — Bruce Lee; E — Ben Kingsley

NOVEMBER 30th

TODAY'S THOUGHT: "Wrinkles should merely indicate where smiles have been." —*Mark Twain*

HISTORY: On this date in 1940 Desi Arnaz proved that he did, in fact, love Lucy by eloping with her to Greenwich, Connecticut.

QUIZ: True or False? Mark Twain was born in Florida.

Trivia
The federal government once spent $50,000 to determine that the average length of a stewardess' nose is 2.6 inches.

QUIZ ANSWER: True — Florida, Missouri that is

DECEMBER 1st

TODAY'S THOUGHT: "I will not eat oysters. I want my food dead. Not sick, not wounded, dead."
—*Woody Allen*

HISTORY: On this date in 1956 the Army made the decision to retire its last combat mule troop.

QUIZ: A two part question: Is the capital of Missouri, according to the state's official definition, pronounced "St. Loo-is" or "St. Looie"; and is it properly written as "St. Louis" or "Saint Louis"?

Trivia
More shoplifters are caught in December than any other month.

QUIZ ANSWER: It is written and pronounced Jefferson City.

DECEMBER 2nd

TODAY'S THOUGHT: "There's one way to find out if a man is honest — ask him. If he says 'yes', you know he's crooked." —*Groucho Marx*

HISTORY: On this date in 1949 Gene Autry hit the record charts with his song "Rudolph, the Red-Nosed Reindeer".

QUIZ: By what name is "Aubergine" better known?

A: Madonna   C: The Vatican
B: Gene Autry   D: Eggplant

Trivia
The most popular cookie is the chocolate chip.

QUIZ ANSWER: D — Eggplant

DECEMBER 3rd

TODAY'S THOUGHT: "If you think it's hard to meet new people, try picking up the wrong golf ball."
—*Jack Lemmon*

HISTORY: On this date in 1967 a team led by Dr. Christian Barnard in Capetown, South Africa performed the first successful human heart transplant. The patient survived 18 days before succumbing of complications.

QUIZ: Bathroom Brain Teaser: Jill had a date with Jack and was waiting for him to pick her up. It began to rain. Jill had no umbrella yet did not get wet. Why?

Trivia
According to a Gallup poll, the most hated food in America is liver.

QUIZ ANSWER: She was waiting inside.

DECEMBER 4th

TODAY'S THOUGHT: "Let us reflect back nostalgically on the past." —*Howard Cosell*

HISTORY: On this date in 1950 Polish track star Stella Walsh, the 1932 Olympic gold medalist in the 100 yard dash, died during an armed robbery at which "she" was an innocent bystander. After the autopsy in Cleveland, Ohio the coroner announced that "she" was a "he".

QUIZ: Which of the following vegetables is not in V-8 juice?
A: Leek   B: Carrot   C: Watercress   D: Beets   E: Celery

Trivia
There is no specific fish called a sardine. Usually you find herring or pilchard in the cans.

QUIZ ANSWER: A — Leek

DECEMBER 5th

TODAY'S THOUGHT: "Girls bored me; they still do. I love Mickey Mouse more than any woman I've ever known." —*Walt Disney*

HISTORY: On this date in 1933 happy days were here again as Prohibition formally ended with the repeal of the 18th Amendment by the 21st.

QUIZ: On average, how much of your life do you spend searching for lost or misplaced items?
A: 3 months B: 6 months C: 9 months D: 1 year

Trivia

According to the International Ice Cream Association, vanilla is by far the most popular flavor. Second is chocolate. And, tied for third, are strawberry and butter pecan.

QUIZ ANSWER: D — The average American loses one year of his life to losing things.

DECEMBER 6th

TODAY'S THOUGHT: "The trouble with growing older is that it gets progressively tougher to find a famous historical figure who didn't amount to much when he was your age." —*Bill Vaughan*

HISTORY: On this date in 1790 Congress moved from New York to Philadelphia. They soon wore out their welcome there as well, and kept going south to Washington D.C.

QUIZ: Without question there is another word, besides facetiously and abstemiously, which contains all the vowels, including "y". What is it?

Trivia

France originated kilts.

QUIZ ANSWER: Unquestionably

DECEMBER 7th

TODAY'S THOUGHT: "The best advice is no _____ at all." —*John Cage*

HISTORY: On this date in 1963 the instant replay was first used in a sports broadcast during the telecast of the Army-Navy game.

QUIZ: True or False? American, Bridal Veil and Horseshoe Falls are names for different types of takedowns in amateur wrestling.

Trivia

Lifesavers candy was invented the same year the Titanic sank.

QUIZ ANSWER: False — They are the three waterfalls which comprise Niagara Falls.

DECEMBER 8th

TODAY'S THOUGHT: "Well, if I called the wrong number, why did you answer the phone?" —*James Thurber*

HISTORY: On this date in 1980 John Lennon was gunned down in New York.

QUIZ: Name these four states: The first begins with "H". The second starts with the last letter of the first state. Continue the same pattern for the third state and for the fourth state — which ends with "Y".

Trivia

The only species of deer that grows horns regardless of its gender is the reindeer. They are also the only species that can grow a red nose and hang out all year with a jolly fat guy at the North Pole.

QUIZ ANSWER: Hawaii—Idaho—Oregon—New Jersey

DECEMBER 9th

TODAY'S THOUGHT: "One loss is good for the soul. Too many losses are not good for the coach." —*Knute Rockne*

HISTORY: On this date in 1907 the Wilmington Post Office sold the very first Christmas seals.

QUIZ: What time of day can make the claim that it is spelled the same forward, backward, upside down and in a mirror?

Trivia
Pocahontas was a family nickname; her real name was Matoaka.

QUIZ ANSWER: NOON

DECEMBER 10th

TODAY'S THOUGHT: "A man finds out what is meant by a spitting image when he tries to feed cereal to his infant." —*Imogene Fey*

HISTORY: On this date in 1927 the Grand Ole Opry hit the airwaves with its first broadcast from WSM in Nashville.

QUIZ: What are gossamer wings?

Trivia
The chance of a mother having quintuplets is 1 in 40,960,000.

QUIZ ANSWER: Just another way of saying cobwebs

DECEMBER 11th

TODAY'S THOUGHT: "If you watch a game, it's fun. If you play it, it's recreation. If you work at it, it's golf."
—*Bob Hope*

HISTORY: On this date in 1980 America got its first look at the latest "Hawaiian Eye" as "Magnum, P.I." premiered on CBS. Diehard fans still celebrate the series at a yearly convention called "Magnum Memorabilia".

QUIZ: Dove il gabinetto? That's an Italian term for people on the go. Do you know the translation?

Trivia
The average human walks 19,000 steps a day.

QUIZ ANSWER: Where's the bathroom?

DECEMBER 12th

TODAY'S THOUGHT: "Never loan shylock money to a woman, because you can't beat her up to collect."
—*Mafia Proverb*

HISTORY: On this date in 1925 the world's first motel, the Motel Inn in San Luis Obispo, California opened for business. It was designed by Arthur Heinman who also coined the term "motel".

QUIZ: Is the Pentagon in Maryland, Virginia or Washington, D.C.?

Trivia
Like humans, dogs can be right-handed or left-handed (or should that be south "paw"?).

QUIZ ANSWER: Virginia

DECEMBER 13th

TODAY'S THOUGHT: "The Lord prefers common-looking people. That is why he makes so many of them."
—*Abraham Lincoln*

HISTORY: On this date in 1816 the first United States savings bank was chartered.

QUIZ: In the January, 1993 issue of "Superman" the comic book hero is killed. What enemy is responsible for his death?

Trivia
Fortune cookies were invented in the U.S. in 1918.

QUIZ ANSWER: Doomsday

DECEMBER 14th

TODAY'S THOUGHT: "A procrastinator is never bothered by the little things that plague the rest of us. He always waits until they grow into big things."
—*Anonymous*

HISTORY: On this date in 1799 George Washington died at Mount Vernon, Virginia at the age of 67.

QUIZ: True or False? All of Elvis Presley's concerts were performed in the United States.

Trivia
There are 225 squares on a Scrabble board.

QUIZ ANSWER: False — The King also appeared in Canada.

DECEMBER 15th

TODAY'S THOUGHT: "If you can count your money, you don't have a billion dollars." —*J. Paul Getty*

HISTORY: On this date in 1939 the world premiere of "Gone With the Wind" took place in Atlanta.

QUIZ: What bathroom-related product earned a permanent place in the hearts and minds of Americans due to a mistake at the factory which allowed too much air to be whipped into it, thus causing it to float?

Trivia
Gamblers have the highest suicide-attempt rate.

QUIZ ANSWER: Ivory soap became a sensation when a worker goofed and let a batch get too much air in it. This soap-serendipity has made it a best seller for over a hundred years.

DECEMBER 16th

TODAY'S THOUGHT: "People are wrong when they say that opera is not what it used to be. It is what it used to be. That's what's wrong with it." —*Noel Coward*

HISTORY: On this date in 1773 colonists dressed as Indians and threw tea in Boston harbor.

QUIZ: What American movie star was Orville Wright's godson?

Trivia
Airplanes are forbidden to fly over the White House.

QUIZ ANSWER: Robert Cummings, who maintained a lifelong interest in aviation

DECEMBER 17th

TODAY'S THOUGHT: "One man's pay increase is another man's price increase." —*Harold Wilson*

HISTORY: On this date in 1777 France recognized the independence of the thirteen American colonies.

QUIZ: Here's a question for presidential trivia buffs: Who was the first president whose mother was eligible to vote for him?

Trivia

New Hampshire has the lowest legal age for marriage; a girl of thirteen can get married with her parents' consent.

QUIZ ANSWER: Franklin Delano Roosevelt

DECEMBER 18th

TODAY'S THOUGHT: "Judge a man not by his clothes, but by his wife's clothes." —*Thomas R. Dewar*

HISTORY: On this date in 1865 ratification of the 13th Amendment, abolishing slavery, was proclaimed.

QUIZ: Bathroom Brain Teaser: The archaeologist said he found a coin dated 84 B.C. How do you know the coin is a phony?

Trivia

The Lovers of the Stinky Rose is an organization that holds an annual garlic festival and publishes a newsletter known as "Garlic Times".

QUIZ ANSWER: The date B.C. was never used before Christ.

DECEMBER 19th

TODAY'S THOUGHT: "Three may keep a secret if two of them are dead." —*Ben Franklin*

HISTORY: On this date in 1732 "Poor Richard's Almanack" began publication in Philadelphia by Ben Franklin.

QUIZ: What is a recidivist?

A: The host of a spelling bee   C: An habitual criminal
B: A diving instructor   D: None of the above

Trivia
The International Lint Museum is in Rutland, Vermont.

QUIZ ANSWER: C — (Speaking of habitual criminals, did you hear about the kleptomaniac who went to the doctor for some help? When he told the doctor his problem, the doctor said, "So, what are you taking for it?")

DECEMBER 20th

TODAY'S THOUGHT: "Zsa Zsa Gabor is an excellent housekeeper. Every time she gets divorced, she keeps the house." —*Henny Youngman*

HISTORY: On this date in 1880 Broadway became the Great White Way as hundreds of electric lights blazed to life between 12th and 26th Streets.

QUIZ: What did Telly Savalas do in show business before he decided to step in front of the cameras?

Trivia
The best-selling prepared dessert in the world is Jell-o.

QUIZ ANSWER: He was a top executive at ABC television, no doubt a job where he developed the expression "Who loves ya, baby?" just before he fired someone.

DECEMBER 21st

TODAY'S THOUGHT: "The sport of skiing consists of wearing three thousand dollars worth of clothes and equipment and driving two hundred miles in the snow in order to stand around at a bar and get drunk."
—P.J. O'Rourke

HISTORY: On this date in 1913 the crossword puzzle made its debut in the New York "World". It was compiled by Arthur Wynne.

QUIZ: How many times does "one" (either in number or word) appear on the dollar bill?

Trivia
Only one out of three people who buy jogging shoes use them for that purpose.

QUIZ ANSWER: 16

DECEMBER 22nd

TODAY'S THOUGHT: "The income tax has made liars out of more Americans than golf." *—Will Rogers*

HISTORY: On this date in 1895 the U.S. Golf Association was formed.

QUIZ: Which of the following names didn't belong to a First Lady?
A: Dolly   B: Mamie   C: Claudia   D: Lou

Trivia
Mel Blanc, the former voice of Bugs Bunny, was allergic to carrots.

QUIZ ANSWER: A — Dolly. Now before you say anything, Mrs. Madison's name was spelled Dolley.
The others were B — Mrs. Eisenhower; C — Mrs. Lady Bird Johnson; D — Mrs. Hoover.

DECEMBER 23rd

TODAY'S THOUGHT: "A cynic is just a man who found out when he was about ten that there wasn't any Santa Claus, and he's still upset."
—*James Gould Cozzens*

HISTORY: On this date in 1823 "A Visit From Saint Nicholas" was first published anonymously and without Clement Moore's knowledge.

QUIZ: True or False? You can be given the death penalty in Arkansas for putting salt on a railroad track.

Trivia
A typical dinner for a whale is 5,000 fish.

QUIZ ANSWER: True — Of course they have to prove that you had the means, opportunity and locomotive.

DECEMBER 24th

TODAY'S THOUGHT: "The three stages of a man's life: 1)He believes in Santa Claus. 2)He doesn't believe in Santa Claus. 3)He is Santa Claus." —*Anonymous*

HISTORY: On this date in 1814 the War of 1812 ended when the U.S. and Great Britain signed the Treaty of Ghent.

QUIZ: Santa Claus is known as "Hoteiosho" in what land?

Trivia
If you get stuck in an elevator during the holiday season, you have more chance of hearing "The Christmas Song" than any other sound of the season.

QUIZ ANSWER: Japan

DECEMBER 25th

TODAY'S THOUGHT: "Santa Claus has the right idea: visit people once a year." — *Victor Borge*

HISTORY: On this date in 1818 "Silent Night" was introduced to the world.

QUIZ: Who is the only actor to win an Oscar for playing Santa Claus?

Trivia
The most Christmas cards ever sent by one person is 62,824.

QUIZ ANSWER: Edmund Gwenn — He won as Best Supporting Actor for his role as St. Nick in "Miracle on 34th Street".

DECEMBER 26th

TODAY'S THOUGHT: "Depend on the rabbit's foot if you must, but remember it didn't work for the rabbit!"
—*R.E. Shaw*

HISTORY: On this date in 1865 James Nason of Franklin, Massachusetts received a patent for the first coffee percolator.

QUIZ: What soda was originally called Patio Diet Cola?

Trivia
David Mullaney of Fairfield, Connecticut invented the Wiffle Ball in 1953.

QUIZ ANSWER: Diet Pepsi

DECEMBER 27th

TODAY'S THOUGHT: "A wife lasts only for the length of the marriage, but an ex-wife is there for the rest of your life." —*Jim Samuels*

HISTORY: On this date in 1932 Radio City Music Hall opened in New York City.

QUIZ: What whale of a story begins with "Call me Ishmael"?

Trivia
One of Louis Pasteur's professors ranked him as barely mediocre in chemistry.

QUIZ ANSWER: "Moby Dick"

DECEMBER 28th

TODAY'S THOUGHT: "For beauty, I'm not a great star.
There are others more handsome by far.
But my face, I don't mind it, for I am behind it;
It's those in front get the jar!" —*Woodrow Wilson*

HISTORY: On this date in 1945 the Pledge of Allegiance was officially recognized by the U.S. Congress.

QUIZ: True or False? Charles Lindbergh was the first pilot to make a non-stop flight across the Atlantic.

Trivia
Ducks and geese can fly at a speed of 70 miles per hour in level flight. In unlevel flight ducks tend to quack up.

QUIZ ANSWER: False — He actually was the 67th. However, he was the first to make the flight alone.

DECEMBER 29th

TODAY'S THOUGHT: "A grouch escapes so many little annoyances that it almost pays to be one."
—*Kin Hubbard*

HISTORY: On this date in 1852 Emma Snodgrass was arrested in Boston and charged with vagrancy because she dared to wear pants.

QUIZ: Vanity license plates have become commonplace among the Baby Boomer set. One such plate was spotted on a car which relates to the occupation of a speech therapist. It reads "BRTQLIT". Can you decipher it?

Trivia

When a black cat crosses your path in Japan, it means good luck.

QUIZ ANSWER: Be articulate

DECEMBER 30th

TODAY'S THOUGHT: "Advertising may be described as the science of arresting human intelligence long enough to get money from it." —*Stephen Leacock*

HISTORY: On this date in 1951 the "Roy Rogers Show" debuted on NBC-TV.

QUIZ: Who lost out on the Captain Kirk role in "Star Trek" because he demanded to own part of the show?

Trivia

Rudyard Kipling paid off the nurse who cared for his child with the manuscript and rights to "The Jungle Book".

QUIZ ANSWER: Jack Lord blew his chance to be Kirk. Instead of warping around the galaxy chasing Klingons he got to go to Hawaii and boss Dano and Chin Ho around.

DECEMBER 31st

TODAY'S THOUGHT: "I have a very good reason for bein' loaded tonight. I been drinkin' all day!"
—*Foster Brooks*

HISTORY: On this date in 1992 a group of 97 people, called the "Time-Tunnellers", saw the New Year in twice by having a party at Shannon, Ireland and leaving at 12:10 on the Concorde for Bermuda, where they arrived at 11:21 p.m. the previous day.

QUIZ: What cowboy and cowgirl were born Leonard Slye and Frances Octavia Smith?

Trivia
A tomato is 95% water.

QUIZ ANSWER: Roy Rogers and Dale Evans, who were married on New Year's Eve in 1947